Grade 5

Treasures

Practice
Book
O

Mc Graw Hill Macmillan
McGraw-Hill

B

The **McGraw·Hill** Companies

 **Macmillan McGraw-Hill**

Published by Macmillan/McGraw-Hill, of McGraw-Hill Education, a division of The McGraw-Hill Companies, Inc., Two Penn Plaza, New York, New York 10121.

Printed in the United States of America

17 18 19 20 RHR 15 14 13 12

Contents

Unit 1 • Challenges

Unit 2 • Discoveries

© Macmillan/McGraw-Hill

Unit 3 • Turning Points

Unit 4 • Experiences

Unit 5 • Achievements

Unit 6 • Great Ideas

© Macmillan/McGraw-Hill

**A. Select the best word from the choices in parentheses.
Then write the correct word on the line provided.**

1. Have you seen the (categories, corners) of talents that will be allowed at

   the talent contest? _____

2. Did you see the size of the stage? It's (slow, gigantic)! _____

3. We walked to the contest in the rain, and now our clothes are (soggy, dry).

   _____

4. The man was tired, so he (slumped, sat up) in his chair and went to sleep.

   _____

5. Cynthia twisted (blocks, strands) of hair around her finger.

   _____

6. If we write a paper, will Mr. Price give us extra (credit, time)?

   _____

7. Our school has lights in front of the stage, so all of the performers have a

   (luminous, dark) glow on their faces. _____

8. All of the performers were quite (splendid, capable) of putting on a good

   show. _____

**B. Write new sentences for two of the vocabulary words
used above. Then underline the vocabulary word.**

9. _____

   _____

10. _____

    _____

Name _____

> The **characters** are the people or animals in a story. The
> **plot** is a series of events that take the characters through an
> experience or change. In some stories the plot includes a
> problem that a character faces and solves.

Read the passage and answer the questions below.

Tuesday I caught a bad cold and had to stay home from school. The next day was Wednesday, and Mrs. Mandle always assigned an essay that day. That afternoon I called my best friend, Roberto. He is a great writer and listens perfectly to Mrs. Mandle's essay questions. However, when I called Roberto, his voice was muffled and what he said wasn't very clear.

"Mike," Roberto said, "the essay is on 'what makes blueberry pies'?"

"What?" I said. "The essay is on 'what makes blueberry pies'?"

"Yes," he said. "I hope you feel butter. I have to go to digger now."

That night I wrote about blueberry pies and how to make them. The next day I felt better and went to school. I saw Roberto and talked about my blueberry pie essay.

"Blueberry pies?" Roberto asked. "We didn't have to write about blueberry pies. Our essay was about 'what makes blue skies.'"

1. Who are the characters in this passage? _____

_____

2. What is Mike's main problem? _____

_____

3. Why does Mike call Roberto for the essay question? _____

_____

_____

4. What could Mike have done differently to solve his essay problem?

_____

_____

At Home: Write a short story about a problem you or someone you know has had. Be sure to develop both character and plot.

As you read *Miss Alaineus*, fill in the Character and Plot Chart.

Character	Plot

How does the information you wrote in this Character and Plot Chart help you analyze the story structure of *Miss Alaineus*?

At Home: Have the student use the chart to retell the story.

Miss Alaineus • Grade 5/Unit I

3

As I read, I will pay attention to pauses and breaks in the text.

	Freddy slapped the table as he snorted. "Check this out,
10	Eva!" he said between chuckles.
15	Freddy grabbed my sketchbook and held it up next to my
26	startled face. Eva frowned, looked confused, and then finally
35	a gigantic smile crossed her face.
41	"You're good, Nadia," she said. "But, I don't get it."
51	What I'd drawn was a cartoon of *me*, with an oversized
62	head and tiny body. I'd added my trademark features.
71	A banner at the top read, "Science UN-Fair." Question marks
81	spun around my head and I had a very confused look—a
93	perfect caricature, I might add.
98	Freddy turned to me and said, "Eva was in the nurse's
109	office during fifth period. Remember? She got hurt playing
118	soccer during lunch."
121	"Oh, yeah," I said. And then I told Eva what she had
133	missed. 134

Comprehension Check

1. Who is the main character of this story? **Character**

2. What did Nadia draw in her sketchbook? **Plot**

	Words Read	–	Number of Errors	=	Words Correct Score
First Read		–		=	
Second Read		–		=	

© Macmillan/McGraw-Hill

At Home: Help the student read the passage, paying attention to the goal at the top of the page.

Name _____

Photographs or drawings provide a visual image of what is happening in the story. **Captions** help explain what the photographs or drawings are about.

Look at the drawing and read the caption. Then answer the questions.

Fifth graders learn about fitness and health by running a one mile race.

1. What does the drawing show? _____

   _____

   _____

2. What other information do you learn from the caption? _____

   _____

   _____

At Home: Find at least three photographs or drawings in magazines or books that do not have captions. Write captions for the images.

Name _____

You can learn the meaning of an unfamiliar word by using the words around it as clues. Look at the words that appear near the word that you don't know, and try to find a **synonym** of that word to help you figure out its meaning. Remember that a synonym is a word with a similar meaning.

Circle the synonym of the underlined word in each sentence.

1. The size of the hot-air balloon <u>decreased</u> and diminished as air was let out of it.

2. The awful sound was <u>unbearable</u> and it woke me up.

3. The roses <u>flourished</u> and thrived more than any other plant in Mrs. Lyon's garden.

4. It can be <u>hazardous</u> to play near a downed power line because electric currents are dangerous.

5. Chris was modest about winning his national award because he is <u>humble</u>.

6. The <u>extravagant</u> party had circus performers, an orchestra, and chefs. Bob thought it was too expensive for only a few guests.

7. The letter was <u>anonymous</u> so the sender is unknown.

8. The basketball team returned <u>victorious</u> because they had won the state championship.

9. The teachers said soda is <u>prohibited</u> because bottles are forbidden in the gym.

10. The paper towel will soak up the spilled milk because it will <u>absorb</u> all the moisture.

© Macmillan/McGraw-Hill

At Home: Write a list of at least three new words from a magazine or book, and use context clues to find a synonym.

The letters *a, e, i, o,* and *u* usually stand for the short vowel sounds /a/ in *damp*, /e/ in *ten*, /i/ in *sit*, /o/ in *hop*, and /u/ in *fun*. Some words with short vowel sounds do not follow this pattern. For example, *ea*, as in *head*, can have the /e/ sound and *ou* followed by *gh*, as in *rough*, can have the /u/ sound.

Place each word in the column that describes the short vowel sound found in the word.

batch	rough	stump	jut	tenth
dove	myth	nick	sense	cot
lead	notch	scan	tough	damp
lot	stamp	sick	fence	rhythm

short **a**	short **e**	short **i**	short **o**	short **u**

© Macmillan/McGraw-Hill

At Home: Work with a parent or helper to add as many words as possible to each column in the chart.

Name _____

A. Choose a word from the box to complete each sentence.

impress	wring	fireball	original
commenced	advertisement	elected	sauntered

1. I just saw an _____ for a new book about Davy Crockett.

2. Davy Crockett packed his bag and _____ his trip.

3. Davy Crockett could easily _____ people because he could do so many things.

4. Davy Crockett had to _____ a dead limb off a big oak tree.

5. Davy Crockett rode a flaming-hot _____ into space.

6. He was _____ to Congress when he received more votes than anyone else.

7. I _____ back to the library, thinking about Davy Crockett as I strolled along.

8. The _____ tall tale about Davy Crockett was told in the 1800s.

B. Write new sentences for two of the vocabulary words used above. Then underline the vocabulary word.

9. _____

   _____

10. _____

   _____

> The **plot** is a series of events that take the characters through an experience or change. In some stories, the plot includes a problem that a character faces. The **setting** is where and when the story takes place.

Read the tall tale below. Tell the setting and the events in the plot.

When a speeding comet threatened to crash into Earth, everyone turned to Davy Crockett for help. Davy Crockett was the biggest, strongest, most courageous man alive. If anyone could save Earth, Davy Crockett could!

Everyone gathered around Davy as he prepared to climb the tallest mountain in Texas. "I'll hop right up to the top of this mountain," he exclaimed, "and grab that comet by the tail. I'll toss it away quicker than you can say 'howdy-do.'"

The people held their breath as Davy took long strides up the mountain. His legs were a blur because they moved so quickly. The crowd gasped when Davy disappeared into the clouds. Would Davy stop the comet?

Just then, the crowd jumped back with a loud roar. Davy had grabbed the comet's tail. He twirled the comet around like a lasso and then sent it flying into outer space.

Davy hadn't even begun to sweat! Davy Crockett proved once again that there was nothing he couldn't do.

Summary: _____

_____

_____

_____

_____

_____

At Home: Summarize one of your favorite stories. Be sure to include details about the setting and problems in the plot.

Davy Crockett Saves the World
Grade 5/Unit I

9

**As you read *Davy Crockett Saves the World*, fill in the
Plot and Setting Chart.**

Plot	Setting

How does the information you wrote in this Plot and Setting Chart help you
analyze the story structure of *Davy Crockett Saves the World*?

© Macmillan/McGraw-Hill

At Home: Have the student use the chart to retell the story.

Name _____

As I read, I will pay attention to punctuation.

	Back then it wasn't easy to feed a large family. Luckily
11	Johnny possessed a green thumb. From the time that he was
22	two years old, it seemed as if Johnny could just look at
34	a seed and a plant commenced to grow. So Johnny and his
46	green thumb fed his large family.
52	There was plenty of food, but dinnertime was extremely
61	noisy in Johnny's house. Why, it was as if a volcano was
73	exploding at dinnertime! As soon as the food hit the table,
84	the children shouted and complained.
89	"Tommy's apple pie is bigger than mine!"
96	"Why are we having apple juice again?"
103	All that noise gave Johnny a headache, so he would take
114	his dinner outside and escape to his favorite spot, the apple
125	orchard. There, Johnny felt at home. 131

Comprehension Check

1. What kind of person is Johnny? **Character**

2. How did Johnny's family benefit from his green thumb? **Plot**

	Words Read	–	Number of Errors	=	Words Correct Score
First Read		–		=	
Second Read		–		=	

At Home: Help the student read the passage, paying attention to the goal at the top of the page.

A **toolbar** is a strip of symbols that allows you to visit different features on a Web site. A **link** is an electronic connection on a Web site that provides direct access to other information.

Use the Web site page to answer the questions.

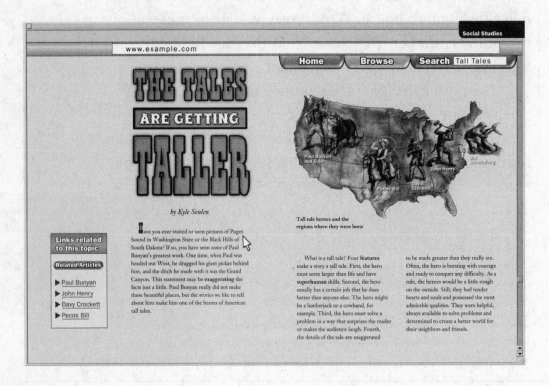

1. Why is the toolbar important? _____

_____

2. What do links do? _____

_____

_____

3. On this Web site, how else would you get information on tall tales?

_____

_____

At Home: Visit a trusted Web site with an adult and examine the toolbar and links.

Name _____

Sometimes two smaller words are put together to form a **compound word.** Recognizing the smaller words can help you figure out the compound word's meaning. For example, *newspaper* is a compound word made from the words *news* and *paper.* The word *newspaper* means "paper on which news is published."

Underline the compound word in each sentence. Then write the compound word's meaning using the meaning of smaller words to help you.

1. The storyteller told an exciting tale about Davy Crockett. _____
   _____

2. One story is about how Pecos Bill tames a whirlwind. _____
   _____

3. I wrote a story about Sluefoot Sue in my notebook. _____
   _____

4. The townspeople decided to ask Davy Crockett for help. _____
   _____

5. We could see for miles from the top of the skyscraper. _____
   _____

6. For dinner, Davy Crockett ate homegrown tomatoes in his salad. _____
   _____

7. Today we will cut the grass with our electric lawnmower. _____
   _____

8. I bought some groceries and a magazine from the shopkeeper. _____
   _____

© Macmillan/McGraw-Hill

At Home: Write five sentences, using one of the compound words above in each.

Words that have the VCe pattern usually have a long vowel sound, as in *fame, mine,* and *bone.* The vowel digraphs *ai* and *ay* usually stand for the long *a* sound, as in *pail* and *play.* The digraphs *ee* and *ea* stand for the long *e* sound, as in *see* and *heap.* The digraphs *oa* and *ow* can stand for the long *o* sound, as in *boat* and *flow.* The vowel *i* can stand for the long *i* sound in words such as *wind, wild.* The letters *igh* in *high* can also stand for the long *i* sound.

A. Write the words from the box that have the same long vowel sound as the first word in each row. Underline the letters that make the long vowel sound.

coach	bike	wheat	pain	may	deep
steam	flight	slate	towing	mind	float

1. rake _____ _____ _____

2. feet _____ _____ _____

3. kite _____ _____ _____

4. flow _____ _____ _____

B. Write a sentence using as many long vowel sound words as possible.

_____

_____

_____

_____

At Home: Look for words with long vowel sounds in a favorite story, magazine, or newspaper. Add at least two more words next to each picture above.

© Macmillan/McGraw-Hill

A. Choose the word from the box that best completes each sentence.

| quest | settings | reduce | buffet | major |

1. Air pollution is a _____ environmental problem.

2. During storms, winds _____ trees causing several of them to fall.

3. Our _____ in the unexplored forest was to find new plants and animals that live there.

4. Rain forests are located in many different kinds of _____, and can be found all over the world.

5. Firefighters try to _____ the number of wildfires by reminding people to watch their campfires closely.

B. Use the sentences in part A to help define these vocabulary words.

6. **settings:** _____

_____

7. **quest:** _____

_____

8. **major:** _____

_____

9. **reduce:** _____

_____

10. **buffet:** _____

_____

One way to organize information in a nonfiction text is to **compare** and **contrast.** When you compare two things, you show how they are similar. When you contrast two things, you show how they are different.

Read the passage below. Then complete the Venn diagram with information about the two kinds of forests.

   Two important biomes, or communities of plants and animals in a particular climate, are the coniferous forest biome and the deciduous forest biome. Coniferous forests are made up primarily of trees that bear cones, such as spruce and fir. Because no leaves fall to the ground and decompose, the soil in coniferous forests is not very rich. Coniferous forests are often found in colder climates in parts of North America, Europe, and Asia.

   Deciduous forests have trees with leaves. Oak and maple trees are found in deciduous forests. When leaves fall to the ground and decay, they make the soil very rich. The climate of a deciduous forest is mild. These forests are also found in North America, Europe, and Asia.

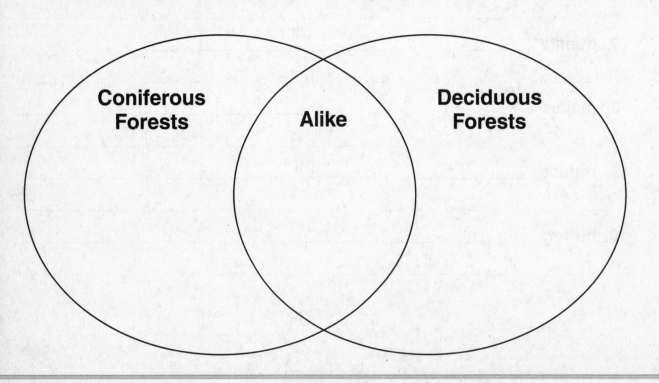

At Home: Work with a parent or helper. Draw pictures of coniferous and deciduous trees.

Name _____

As you read "Forests of the World", fill in the Venn Diagram.

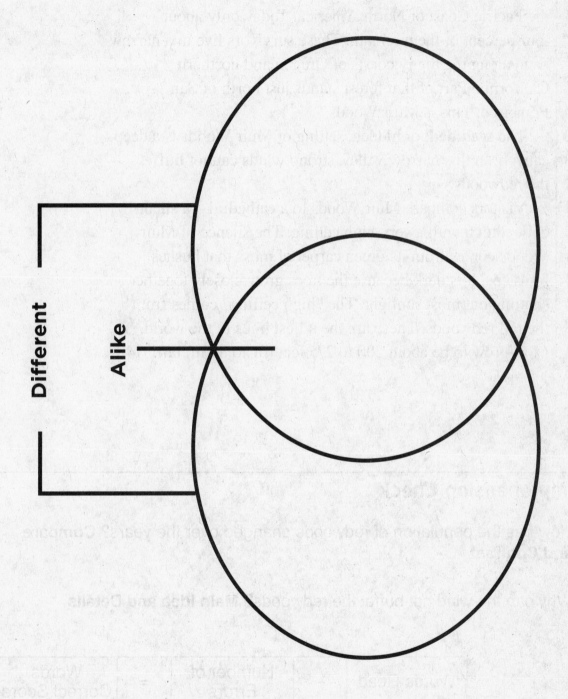

Different

Alike

How does the information you wrote in this Venn Diagram help you analyze text structure of "Forests of the World"?

At Home: Have the student use the chart to retell the story.

Forests of the World • Grade 5/Unit 1   17

As I read, I will pay attention to pronunciation.

	Two thousand years ago, redwood forests stretched along
8	the Pacific Coast of North America. Today only about
17	four percent of them remain. These survivors live in a narrow
28	band along the foggy coasts of Oregon and northern
37	California. Part of that forest stands just north of San
47	Francisco. This is Muir Woods.
52	The **secluded**, or hidden, setting of Muir Woods is a deep
63	canyon. In this narrow valley, strong winds cannot **buffet**
72	the redwoods.
74	Visitors compare Muir Woods to a cathedral—a silent,
83	dark church with a very high ceiling. The silence of Muir
94	Woods comes from its green carpet of moss that hushes
104	footsteps. It is dark because the trees grow closely together,
114	shutting out most sunlight. The "high ceiling" comes from
123	the tall redwoods. These are the tallest trees in the world.
134	Most grow to be about 200 to 275 feet (61 to 84 m) tall. 143

Comprehension Check

1. How has the population of redwoods changed over the years? **Compare and Contrast**

2. Why can the wind not buffet the redwoods? **Main Idea and Details**

	Words Read	–	Number of Errors	=	Words Correct Score
First Read		–		=	
Second Read		–		=	

At Home: Help the student read the passage, paying attention to the goal at the top of the page.

A **library** often holds more than collections of books and magazines. Due to advances in technology, information can be stored and presented in many different forms. To use a library or **media center** successfully, choose the correct resources.

Choose the resource from the chart that would provide useful information for each item below. Write the name of the resource on the line provided.

Sample of Media Center Resources
Thomas Pakenham's book of photographs about trees around the world
online encyclopedia, key words "wildfire" and "containment"
CD entitled *The Music of the Brazilian Rain Forest*
video documentary called *Three Forest Biomes and the Animals that Live in Them*
print encyclopedia, volume B, article about common trees
CD-ROM entitled *Maps, Geography, and the Environment*

1. Which resource would you use to read articles about these common trees in the United States: black cherry, box elder, black willow?

   _____

2. Which resource would you use to hear what a typical day in a rain forest sounds like? _____

   _____

3. Which resource would you use to find pictures of a tree named "General Sherman" in California and a tree called a "dancing lime" in Germany? _____

   _____

4. Which resource would you use to learn about techniques used to control wildfires? _____

   _____

At Home: Choose a topic to find information about using one of the resources, and write a short paragraph about your topic.

Forests of the World • Grade 5/Unit 1   19

Sometimes words have one spelling but two distinct pronunciations and two different meanings. These words are called **homographs.** You can use a dictionary to learn the different definitions and pronunciations of a homograph. For example, if you look up the word **bass** in a dictionary, you will find that it is a kind of fish (pronounced with a short *a* vowel sound). You will also find that **bass** pronounced with a long *a* vowel sound) refers to a deep sound or tone.

Use a dictionary to write the meanings and pronunciations of these homographs.

Word	Pronunciation	Definition
1. buffet	a. _____	_____
	b. _____	_____
2. bow	a. _____	_____
	b. _____	_____
3. tear	a. _____	_____
	b. _____	_____
4. wind	a. _____	_____
	b. _____	_____
5. object	a. _____	_____
	b. _____	_____

At Home: Work with a parent or helper. Think of at least two more homographs. Use a dictionary to find their meanings and pronunciations, and write them down.

© Macmillan/McGraw-Hill

Name _____

- The vowel *u* in *tuna*, the vowels *oo* in *soon*, and the letters *ew* in *grew* can stand for the /ü/ sound. The VCe pattern in *plume* can also stand for the /ü/ sound.
- The vowel *u* in *music*, the vowels *ue* in *cue*, the letters *ew* in *few*, and the VCe pattern in *cute* can also stand for the /ū/ sound.
- The vowels *oo* can also stand for the /ù/ sound in *book*.

Read each sentence. Circle the word that has the vowel sounds in *loon*, *mule*, or *book*. Then write the word in the column for that vowel sound.

1. It is important to prune a tree's branches.

2. Don't fasten those hooks to the tree branches!

3. The wildfire has a deep yellow hue.

4. My handbook about trees has great pictures.

5. We plant a few trees in the park each year.

6. Some flutes are made from trees.

7. This tree will provide wood for the people.

8. There are many ways to use that timber.

9. The horse carried the food up the hill.

l**oo**n /ü/	m**u**le /ū/	b**oo**k /ù/

At Home: Look in your textbook for more words that have these sounds. Add at least two more words to each column of the chart.

Forests of the World • **Grade 5/Unit 1** 21

Name _____

A. Match each vocabulary word with its definition. Write the vocabulary word on the line provided.

mission	function	maze	environment
disasters	gravity	adjusted	zone

1. the air, water, soil, and all the other things surrounding a person, animal or plant _____

2. special assignment or job _____

3. changed or rearranged _____

4. terrible and unexpected events _____

5. a confusing system of paths or passageways _____

6. to work properly _____

7. the force that attracts objects to Earth _____

8. an area set off from other areas _____

B. Answer each question.

9. Why is **gravity** important? _____

_____

_____

10. How might a **maze** slow you down? _____

_____

_____

When you **summarize** nonfiction, you retell it briefly in your own words. In the retelling you focus on the most important ideas or events in the passage. The main idea of a paragraph is often found in the first sentence. Supporting details tell you more about a paragraph's main idea. A summary should include important details that describe or explain the main ideas.

Read the two paragraphs below, and then write a summary of the passage on the lines provided. Be sure to include the most important ideas and supporting details in your summary.

Becoming an Astronaut

Astronauts must go through difficult training because just about everything is done differently in space. Astronauts must learn how to walk and work without gravity. They must practice wearing spacesuits. They must even learn how to eat and sleep while weightless.

Many different machines help the astronauts prepare for space travel. Some machines are simulators, or machines that recreate some of the conditions of outer space here on Earth. The 1/6 Gravity Chair simulates the moon's weaker gravity. On the moon a person weighs one-sixth of what he or she weighs on Earth. In the Multi-Axis Trainer (MAT), astronauts experience what it is like to be in a tumbling spacecraft. The Five Degrees of Freedom (5DF) Chair simulates the challenges of floating weightlessly.

Summary: _____

_____

_____

_____

_____

_____

© Macmillan/McGraw-Hill

At Home: With a parent or helper, choose a paragraph in a book, magazine, or newspaper. Write a short summary.

As you read *Ultimate Field Trip 5,* **fill in the Summary Chart.**

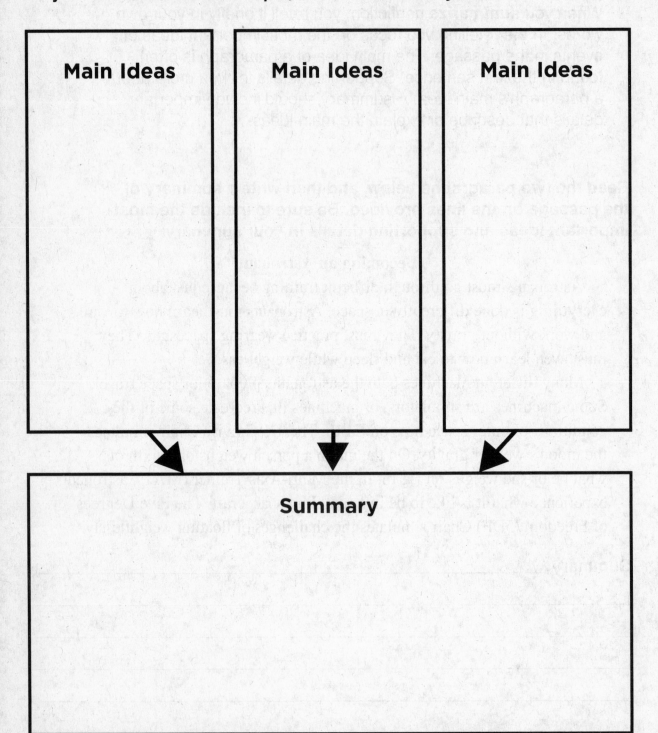

| Main Ideas | Main Ideas | Main Ideas |

Summary

How does the information you wrote in this Summary Chart help you generate questions about *Ultimate Field Trip 5?*

Ultimate Field Trip 5: Blasting Off
to Space Academy • **Grade 5/Unit 1**

At Home: Have the student use the chart to retell the story.

© Macmillan/McGraw-Hill

As I read, I will pay attention to pronunciation.

	People on Earth have long looked at Mars with excitement
10	and fear. Mars is Earth's nearest neighbor and has an
20	environment similar to Earth's in many ways. The surface
29	of Mars is much like the surface of parts of Earth, dry and
42	hard. Temperatures on Mars range from –225° to 60°
49	Fahrenheit (-140° to 25° Celsius). There are important
55	differences, too. The atmosphere of Mars is almost all carbon
65	dioxide and doesn't have enough oxygen to support humans.
74	On Mars, **gravity,** the force that pulls us toward the ground,
85	is not as strong as gravity on Earth.
93	However, of all the planets in the solar system, Mars
103	is the one that seems most possible for humans to visit and
115	even colonize. It is close to us, and it has a surface and
128	surface temperature most similar to that of Earth. 136

Comprehension Check

1. Why does Mars seem like the most likely planet for humans to visit? **Main Idea and Details**

2. What are some differences between Earth and Mars? **Compare and Contrast**

	Words Read	–	Number of Errors	=	Words Correct Score
First Read		–		=	
Second Read		–		=	

At Home: Have the student read the passage, paying attention to the goal at the top of the page.

Name _____

Practice

Literary Elements:
Rhyme Scheme
and Rhythm

When you read poetry, pay attention to the poem's **rhyme scheme** and **rhythm.** The rhyme scheme is a pattern of words that have the same ending sound, such as *light* and *tight*. Rhythm is the regular repetition of accented or stressed syllables in the lines of a poem. Rhythm gives the poem a steady beat, almost like that of music.

A. In the poem below, fill in the blanks by choosing a word from the list that completes the rhyme scheme. Write the word on the lines provided.

| right | round | glow | roar |

1. We're in the rocket, set to go.

   The lift-off lights begin to _____.

2. The engines rumble, then they _____.

   Can we still run right out the door?

3. The spacecraft rolls from left to _____.

   And soon we rocket out of sight.

4. But wait! It's over. We're all safe and sound.

   Oh, it was just the simulator spinning _____.

B. Identify the rhythm in these lines of the poem. Underline the accented syllables.

The spacecraft rolls from left to right.
And soon we rocket out of sight.
But wait! It's over. We're all safe and sound.
Oh, it was just the simulator spinning round.

At Home: Read a poem aloud to hear the rhythm. Make a list of the words that rhyme.

Name _____

If you are reading and come to an unfamiliar word, look at the other words in the sentence. These words might give you hints as to the meaning of the unfamiliar word. We call these hints **context clues.** For example, context clues might explain or describe an unfamiliar word.

Use context clues to help define the underlined words in the passage. Circle the letter of the response that best completes each sentence.

1. At the U.S. Space Academy, we felt what it was like to be <u>weightless</u> and float through the air.

   If you are weightless, you are not affected by _____.

   a. air   **b.** gravity   **c.** space

2. Astronauts use <u>simulators</u> in order to feel like what it will be like in space.

   What are simulators _____?

   a. machines   **b.** portals   **c.** missions

3. Since space has no <u>atmosphere</u>, special suits need to be worn to supply astronauts with air and protect them from the sun.

   The special suits provide _____.

   a. sunlight and gravity   **b.** gas and bubbles   **c.** protection from the sun and air

4. The mission crew was asked to <u>deploy</u> the robot that was being stored to work on a broken satellite.

   The robot was deployed to complete an _____.

   a. operation   **b.** orbit   **c.** astronaut

5. Someday it might be possible to <u>colonize</u> the moon so people could live there.

   You cannot colonize a place without _____.

   a. sidewalks   **b.** people   **c.** bikes

At Home: Choose three of the underlined words above. Write a sentence with new context clues for each word. Share your sentences with a parent or helper.

Ultimate Field Trip 5: Blast Off to Space Academy • Grade 5/Unit 1

27

© Macmillan/McGraw-Hill

- The letters *ar* usually stand for the /är/ sound in *car* and *carve*.
- The letters *ear* and *are* can stand for the /âr/ sound in *bear* and *care*.
- The letters *or, ore, oar, our* can stand for the /ôr/ sound in *for, core, roar,* and *your*.

A. Underline the words in the paragraph that have the /är/ sound in *car*, /âr/ sound in *bear*, or the /ôr/ sound in *for*. Then sort them on the chart below.

The astronauts climbed aboard their space ship. They wore space suits made from special fabric. Their goal was to travel far into space and explore a nearby star. During the flight, they had many chores to do. They also had to take care not to tear holes in their suits.

B. Sort the underlined words in the paragraph according to the vowel + *r* sound.

/är/ sound in *car*	/âr/ sound in *bear*	/ôr/ sound in *for*
_____	_____	_____
_____	_____	_____
_____	_____	_____
_____	_____	_____

At Home: Work with a parent or helper. Make three lists: one of *ar* sounds, one of *or* sounds, and one of *are* sounds. Write new words in each column.

Name _____

Choose the vocabulary word that best replaces the underlined word or words. Write your choice on the line provided.

| fragrance | celebration | variety | moistened |
| cooperation | canceled | theory | transformed |

1. One <u>possible explanation</u> for the roof dogs' disappearance was that they flew off into the night. _____

2. If you have a <u>collection of different types</u> of dogs, some will most likely be working dogs. _____

3. When called into action, the search-and-rescue dog <u>changed</u> from a friendly pet into a life-saving hero. _____

4. There is usually a <u>joyful party</u> at the animal shelter when a dog finds a new home. _____

5. Most dogs can smell any <u>odor</u> or <u>pleasant scent</u>. _____

6. With <u>shared efforts</u>, the dog and the park rangers found the lost camper. _____

7. Even when rain has <u>dampened</u> a scent trail, dogs with good noses will be able to follow the smell. _____

8. The search was <u>called off</u> when a dog found the missing person in the woods. _____

© Macmillan/McGraw-Hill

Name _____

> A **cause** is the reason why something happens. An **effect** is the result, or what happens. Many story events are connected through cause-and-effect relationships. Signal words such as *because, so, as a result* help readers identify cause-and-effect relationships.

Read the passage. On the lines below, write the most likely cause or effect.

Sherri's collie, Hap, was a talented herding dog. Hap's job was to run out to the field and gather the sheep every morning and evening. Hap nudged the sheep to get them to move.

One evening Hap ran up to Sherri, barking wildly and running in circles. Sherri grabbed her coat and ran after the dog. Hap led Sherri out to the field. None of the sheep were moving. Sherri followed Hap to the edge of a deep hole. "Now I see what's wrong," Sherri said. She slid down into the hole next to a little lamb that couldn't get out. "Good job, Hap," she said. Sherri carried the frightened creature out of the hole.

Sherri released the lamb back into the herd. The sheep started to move, and Hap urged them along. Now everyone would go home together.

1. **Cause:** _____

   Effect: The sheep walked from the field to the ranch.

2. **Cause:** Hap barked wildly and ran in circles.

   Effect: _____

3. **Cause:** Hap ran to the hole.

   Effect: _____

4. **Cause:** _____

   Effect: The sheep finally started to move.

© Macmillan/McGraw-Hill

At Home: Read an article in a newspaper aloud to a parent or helper. Write down examples of cause-and-effect relationships in the article.

As you read *Pipiolo and the Roof Dogs,* fill in the Cause and Effect Chart.

Cause	➡️	Effect
	➡️	
	➡️	
	➡️	
	➡️	

How does the information you wrote in this Cause and Effect Chart help you generate questions about *Pipiolo and the Roof Dogs*?

At Home: Have the student use the chart to retell the story.

Pipiolo and the Roof Dogs
Grade 5/Unit 1

31

As I read, I will pay attention to tempo.

	"It's finally here!" I said to myself as I got off the school
13	bus that Friday afternoon. "And it's going to be great!"
23	I had been patient. I'd waited and waited for the big
34	family party. It was just one day away. From all over the city
47	and even as far away as Baltimore, my family was meeting
58	at our house for a cookout supper Saturday night. My older
69	sister, Mai, was excited, too. She had promised to decorate our
80	backyard and even string little lights all over the trees and
91	bushes. We'd start today, and then finish up tomorrow
100	morning before her big soccer game. I never missed Mai's
110	soccer games. She and her team were the city champions,
120	and their games were really fun to watch.
128	But now it was time to decorate the yard. 137

Comprehension Check

1. Why is the narrator excited? **Cause and Effect**

2. What is Mai's responsibility for the party? **Plot**

	Words Read	−	Number of Errors	=	Words Correct Score
First Read		−		=	
Second Read		−		=	

© Macmillan/McGraw-Hill

At Home: Have the student read the passage, paying attention to the goal at the top of the page.

Charts are useful to organize and display information. Charts allow you to list a series of things in one column and information about those things in other columns. A chart usually has headings at the top of each column to describe the information the columns contain.

Use the chart about different dog breeds to answer the questions below.

Dogs with Jobs		
Breed	**Originally Used For . . .**	**Now Often Used To . . .**
Welsh Corgi	driving other people's cattle off protected land	gather livestock and herd animals home
Dalmatian	running beside coaches to clear a path for the horses	be companion animals
Newfoundland	dragging carts and carrying heavy loads	rescue people from water
golden retriever	picking up game for hunters	serve as guide dogs for people who are blind

1. What task did golden retrievers originally perform? _____

_____

2. How are Dalmatians put to use today? _____

_____

3. How is a Welsh Corgi's job today different from its original job? _____

_____

_____

4. Which breed is now known for rescuing people in the water? _____

_____

5. Which breed is often used to help people who are blind? _____

_____

At Home: Make a chart called "People that I Know." Under the heading "Names," list three names. Use "Job" as another heading and fill in the chart.

Pipiolo and the Roof Dogs
Grade 5/Unit 1

33

© Macmillan/McGraw-Hill

Synonyms are words that have very similar meanings. A thesaurus contains lists of synonyms. A dictionary often includes synonyms for a word along with the word's definition.

> **aroma** *n.* smell, scent, odor
> **brave** *adj.* courageous, fearless
> **dog** *n.* hound, mutt, pooch
> **village** *n.* metropolis, town, city

Use the thesaurus entries in the box to find synonyms for the underlined word in each sentence. Rewrite each sentence using one of the synonyms.

1. The <u>aroma</u> of baking bread made my mouth water.

_____

_____

2. The <u>brave</u> firefighter rescued three people from the burning building.

_____

_____

3. Our <u>village</u> was growing larger and larger as new people moved in.

_____

_____

4. We saw a spotted <u>dog</u> with long fur sitting by our door.

_____

_____

At Home: Work with a parent or helper to think of two synonyms for each of the following words: *village, yelp, delight, tired,* and *courage.*

© Macmillan/McGraw-Hill

Practice

Name _____

Phonics: Words with /ûr/ and /îr/

The letters *ur, er, ir,* or *ear* can stand for the /ûr/ sound in *fur, her, bird,* and *earn*. The letters *ear* and *eer* can stand for the /îr/ sound, as in *fear* and *deer*.

A. Place each word in the column that best represents its vowel sound.

| squirm | dreary | engineer | verse | clear |
| nerve | lurch | learn | sneer | ear |

fur /ûr/	*fear* /îr/
1. _____	6. _____
2. _____	7. _____
3. _____	8. _____
4. _____	9. _____
5. _____	10. _____

B. Answer the questions using the chart above.

11. How can the /ûr/ sound be spelled?

_____

12. How can the /îr/ sound be spelled?

_____

At Home: With a parent or helper, make a list of *ûr* or *îr* words. Write a sentence for at least five new words.

| celebration | gigantic | impress | quest | disasters |

A. Complete the following sentences using words from the box.

1. Davy was on a _____ to save the world from destruction.

2. A _____ meteor was headed straight for Earth.

3. He never tried to _____ anyone with his amazing strength.

4. Earthquakes and hurricanes are examples of natural _____.

5. His friends held a big _____ to show their thanks.

B. Write a sentence of your own for each of the following words.

6. slumped _____

_____

7. settings _____

_____

8. wring _____

_____

9. adjusted _____

_____

10. variety _____

_____

© Macmillan/McGraw-Hill

A. Read each question, and circle the letter of your answer.

1. Which of the following best describes someone slumped in a chair?

   a. alert   **b.** drooping

   c. proper

2. Which of the following would impress a teacher?

   a. a well-written paper   **b.** a low score on a test

   c. falling asleep during class

3. What happens when strong winds buffet trees?

   a. the trees die   **b.** the trees get knocked about

   c. the winds have no effect

4. If a towel has been moistened, how will it feel to the touch?

   a. warm   **b.** scratchy

   c. damp

5. In what type of environment do most students spend their day?

   a. a forest   **b.** a gymnasium

   c. a classroom

B. Use each of the following words in a sentence.

1. luminous _____

_____

2. sauntered _____

_____

3. function _____

_____

4. gravity _____

_____

5. fragrance _____

_____

Name _____

Use the correct word from the list.

injury	mournful	sympathy	delivering
slurp	shrieks	decency	bulletin board

1. The mother felt _____ toward the hawk.

2. The boy was delighted to put a picture of the hawk on the

   _____.

3. Did you hear the _____ of all those birds?

4. I saw them _____ the hawk to the veterinarian.

5. The hawk had suffered an _____ but was going to survive.

6. The mother and child had the _____ to stop the car and take care of the hawk.

7. The mother took one long _____ and finished her smoothie.

8. People can become very _____ when they see injured animals.

Use the vocabulary words to answer the questions.

9. **bulletin board**   Why is a bulletin board a good place to put important things or notices?

   _____

   _____

10. **mournful**   What does it mean to be mournful?

    _____

    _____

Name _____

An inference is a conclusion or deduction made from evidence.
Readers **make inferences** about story elements based on details
in the story or from their own experience. You usually "read between
the lines" to figure out what a character is feeling or intends to do.
When you make judgments or conclusions based on your reading,
you are making inferences about characters or events.

Read the selection. Then make inferences to answer the questions.

Maria walked into the kitchen with a frown on her face. Her mother was
standing over the counter, chopping red peppers. Maria sat down on a
small stool.

Maria's mother looked up from her cutting board. "Maria, you need to
cheer up. Rowdy wasn't your dog. It's not fair for you to keep him."

"I know," Maria began. "I'll be all right. I'll just miss when Rowdy jumps
on my belly when I'm lying on the floor. I'll miss when he curls up in that
shoe box. I'll just miss him."

Maria's mother stopped chopping and walked over beside her daughter.
"Sweetie, don't you worry. Your birthday is right around the corner and I
know just what to get you."

Maria's face lit up. "Oh, mom!" she exclaimed, hugging her mother.

1. How is Maria feeling in the beginning of the story? How do you know?

_____

2. How is Maria feeling at the end of the story? How do you know?

_____

3. How big is Rowdy? How do you know?

_____

4. What do you think will happen on Maria's birthday?

_____

At Home: Pick your favorite character from a movie or story.
Then make inferences about how that character would act at
a birthday party and explain why.

Name _____

As you read *Shiloh*, fill in the Inferences Chart.

Text Clues	What You Know	Inferences

How does the information you wrote in this Inferences Chart help you
monitor comprehension of *Shiloh*?

 At Home: Have the student use the chart to retell the story.

Name _____

As I read, I will pay attention to punctuation.

	Just past the admissions window, not far from a display of
11	llamas, Mrs. Battaglia assembled her students. She blew her
20	nose, cleared her throat, and said, "There are ten endangered
30	animals here at the zoo. *Achoo!*"
36	"Bless you," someone muttered.
40	"Thank you. In groups of three, you are to visit them and
52	answer all of the questions on your worksheet."
60	Alice noticed that Mrs. Battaglia's eyes were red and
69	tearing. She glanced at Wendy, who giggled. For all her talk
80	about their fascinating blood cells, Mrs. Battaglia was clearly
89	too allergic to go anywhere near actual animals.
97	"At the end of today, your group will choose one—*achoo!*—
108	animal. It will be your assignment to find a way to raise
120	money for that animal at the school fundraiser in two weeks."
131	Wendy grabbed Alice's hand. "Let's go together," she
139	said. 140

Comprehension Check

1. What does allergic mean in this passage? **Context Clues**

2. How do you think Mrs. Battaglia feels about the field trip to the zoo? **Make Inferences**

	Words Read	–	Number of Errors	=	Words Correct Score
First Read		–		=	
Second Read		–		=	

At Home: Help the student read the passage, paying attention to the goal at the top of the page.

Shiloh • **Grade 5/Unit 2**   **41**

© Macmillan/McGraw-Hill

A **photograph** can help you see what a story or article is explaining or describing. The photograph's **caption** provides more information about what you see in the photograph.

Look at the photograph, read the caption, and then put a check beside the statements that would be included in the article.

People come to choose and adopt animals at the animal shelter.

1. _____ Ten dogs, five cats, seven kittens, and twelve puppies were adopted in all.

2. _____ The Lions Club will be holding their annual fair from July 30 through August 4.

3. _____ There was a clown giving out balloons and a cowboy offering free pony rides.

4. _____ There was an Adoption Fair at the Third Street animal shelter today.

5. _____ Eleven-year-old Richard Vitarelli went home with a beagle pup.

6. _____ People were encouraged to take prospective pets out of their crates and get acquainted with the animals.

© Macmillan/McGraw-Hill

At Home: Go through newspapers or magazines to find photographs and captions. Explain how the photographs help you understand more about the story.

An **idiom** is a phrase that cannot be understood from the meaning of the separate words in it. You can often find idioms in the dictionary.

A. Match each idiom to what it means. Then write the correct letter on the line provided.

1. _____ At the eleventh hour

2. _____ Beat around the bush

3. _____ Jump to a conclusion

4. _____ Until you're blue in the face

a. decide something quickly without thinking about it

b. forever

c. avoiding an issue or avoiding giving an answer

d. at the last minute

B. Circle the idiom in each sentence. Write the meaning of the idiom on the next line.

5. It's important to keep your chin up even if your team is losing the big game.

_____

6. My best friend moved far away so I am feeling blue.

_____

7. Jose is a go-getter so it wasn't a shock when he was elected student president.

_____

8. Rain or shine the picnic will happen tomorrow.

_____

At Home: Draw a picture depicting one of the idioms above.

A. Make a compound word. Fill in the equation using the words from the box in order to make the best compound word. Write the compound word on the last line.

| place | cake | parent | print | shore |
| paper | ball | burger | quake | yard |

1. news + _____ = _____

2. base + _____ = _____

3. earth + _____ = _____

4. ham + _____ = _____

5. finger + _____ = _____

6. back + _____ = _____

7. fire + _____ = _____

8. pan + _____ = _____

9. grand + _____ = _____

10. sea + _____ = _____

B. Split each compound word into two smaller words. Write each word on the lines provided.

11. overcrowded: _____ _____

12. password: _____ _____

13. commonplace: _____ _____

14. zookeeper: _____ _____

15. tumbleweed: _____ _____

At Home: Together with a parent or helper, write a sentence using as many of these compound words as possible.

A. From each pair of words below, circle the word that best completes the sentence. Then write the correct word on the line provided.

1. Snakes are (predators / reptiles) because they live by hunting and eating other animals. _____

2. There are about 30 (brands / species) of rattlesnake. _____

3. A rattler shakes its tail as a warning before (fleeing / lunging) toward you. _____

4. You can (survive / avoid) a snake bite if you get help right away. _____

5. Snakes can feel another animal approaching because the ground (vibrates / twists). _____

6. Rattlesnakes often blend in with their (surroundings / forests), which makes them hard to see. _____

7. The hikers were (unprepared / alert) after rattlesnakes were spotted on the trail. _____

8. A rattlesnake shoots poison through its fangs when it bites its (prey / venom). _____

B. Write new sentences for two of the vocabulary words used above. Then underline the vocabulary word.

9. _____

_____

10. _____

_____

> The **main idea** is the most important point an author makes in the story. **Details** are facts that support this main idea and are found throughout the story. By recognizing the main idea and details, you will be able to easily remember the most important information about a story.

The introductory paragraphs below come from "Rattlers!" Read the paragraphs and answer the questions about the main idea and supporting details.

Rattlesnakes have a bad reputation. No wonder! They look mean. They sound spooky. And you know about their nasty bite. But mostly they're misunderstood. So here is all you ever wanted to know about rattlesnakes.

They are a group of snakes that have what no other snakes have: rattle-tipped tails. They also have thick bodies, wide heads, cat-like eyes, and long, hollow fangs that fold away when they're not needed. Their dull colors and patchy patterns help them blend with their surroundings.

1. After reading the paragraphs, what do you think is the main idea of "Rattlers!"? Circle the letter of your answer.

   a. Rattlesnakes are poisonous snakes that eat other animals.

   b. Rattlesnakes have a bad reputation because they are misunderstood.

   c. People must be brave to study rattlesnakes in the wild.

2. List three details about the characteristics of rattlesnakes that support the main idea.

   a. _____

   _____

   b. _____

   _____

   c. _____

   _____

© Macmillan/McGraw-Hill

At Home: With a family member or helper, read a newspaper or magazine article. Underline the article's main idea and discuss the details that support the main idea.

Name _____

As you read a section of "Rattlers!", fill in the Main Idea Web.

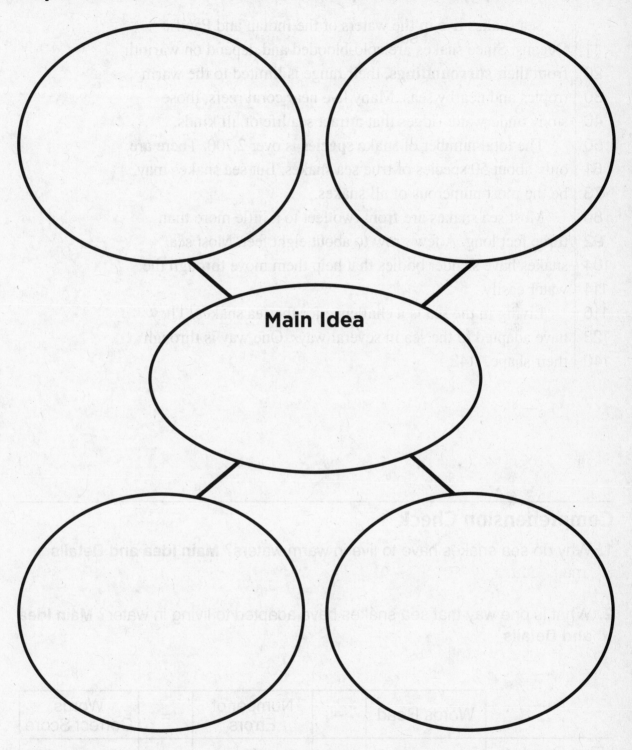

Main Idea

How does the information you wrote in this Main Idea Web help you summarize the section of "Rattlers!" you chose?

At Home: Have the student use the chart to retell the story.

Rattlers! • Grade 5/Unit 2   47

© Macmillan/McGraw-Hill

As I read, I will pay attention to punctuation.

	Sea snakes live in the waters of the Indian and Pacific
11	Oceans. Since snakes are cold-blooded and depend on warmth
20	from their **surroundings,** their range is limited to the warm
30	tropics and nearby seas. Many live near coral reefs, those
40	stony underwater ridges that attract sea life of all kinds.
50	The total number of snake **species** is over 2,700. There are
61	only about 50 species of true sea snakes. But sea snakes may
73	be the most numerous of all snakes.
80	Most sea snakes are from two feet to a little more than
92	three feet long. A few grow to about eight feet. Most sea
104	snakes have slender bodies that help them move through the
114	water easily.
116	Living in the sea is a challenge for the sea snakes. They
128	have adapted to the sea in several ways. One way is through
140	their shape. 142

Comprehension Check

1. Why do sea snakes have to live in warm waters? **Main Idea and Details**

2. What is one way that sea snakes have adapted to living in water? **Main Idea and Details**

	Words Read	–	Number of Errors	=	Words Correct Score
First Read		–		=	
Second Read		–		=	

© Macmillan/McGraw-Hill

At Home: Help the student read the passage, paying attention to the goal at the top of the page.

Name _____

Legends are stories that come down from the past, based on the traditions of a people or region. The **hero** is the main character in a legend, who often does something brave to help others. **Personification** is the assignment of human characteristics to an animal, a thing, or an idea.

Read the following passage from "How Poison Came into the World." Answer the questions on the lines provided.

Long ago, when the Earth was young, the Choctaw people loved to swim in the cool waters on the bayou. But the Choctaw had to be very careful when swimming because a poisonous plant grew in the heart of the bayou. This plant lived below the surface of the water, so swimmers could not see it until it was too late.

The plant, however, did not want to hurt his friends the Choctaw. As more people fell ill, the poor plant became sadder and sadder. Finally, he decided to give away his poison. The plant called the chiefs of the wasps and snakes to meet with him. He asked them to take his poison.

1. Who is the hero in "How Poison Came into the World"? Explain your answer.

_____

_____

2. How is the plant personified? _____

_____

3. How does the legend reflect a certain region or people? _____

_____

4. What sacrifice do you think the plant will make? _____

_____

_____

5. What is the point of this legend? _____

_____

At Home: Think about "How Poison Came into the World" and draw a picture from the legend. Share your picture with a family member or helper, and tell him or her what the legend explains.

Rattlers! • Grade 5/Unit 2   **49**

As you read, you can use **context clues** to help you define unfamiliar words. Context clues restate what unfamiliar words mean.

Look for context clues to help you define the underlined word in each sentence. Then write the meaning of the underlined word on the line provided.

1. Many <u>species</u>, or kinds, of rattlesnake are found in the United States.

   _____

2. A rattlesnake shoots <u>venom</u>, or poison, through its fangs when it bites.

   _____

3. Rattlers blend in with their <u>surroundings</u> because their dull colors and patchy skin match their environment. _____

4. The fangs of a rattlesnake fold away when they're <u>unnecessary</u>, or not needed. _____

5. Rattlesnakes use <u>pits</u>, or dents, on their heads to sense the body heat of other animals. _____

6. When a rattlesnake shakes its tail, the rattle <u>vibrates</u> and makes noise.

   _____

7. Snakes can move quickly, even though they just <u>slither</u>, or slide, along.

   _____

8. Some animals are not <u>bothered</u>, or harmed, by rattlesnake venom.

   _____

© Macmillan/McGraw-Hill

At Home: Write sentences using the following vocabulary words: **predators, alert,** and **lunging.** Make sure each sentence includes context clues.

Add the letter **s** to most words to make them plural. Add **-es** to words that end in **s, x, z, ch,** or **sh** to form plurals. For example, **bunch** becomes **bunches.** When a word ends in the letter **y** and has a consonant before the **y,** change the **y** to **i** and then add **-es.** For example, the plural form of **bunny** is **bunnies.**

A. Write the plural form of each word on the line provided.

1. risk _____

2. century _____

3. compass _____

4. ability _____

5. rattler _____

6. loss _____

7. academy _____

8. tax _____

B. Look at each plural word below. Then write the singular form of the word on the line provided.

9. tongues _____

10. pouches _____

11. babies _____

12. forests _____

13. stories _____

14. branches _____

15. dictionaries _____

At Home: With a family member or helper, list six more words that need -es to become plural.

A. Write the word that best completes each sentence.

dedicated	artifacts	site	exhibits	equality

1. When the museum was _____, people gave speeches at the ceremony.

2. A monument should be at a _____, or location, that everyone can reach easily.

3. People can learn from the past by viewing items in museum

   _____.

4. Objects, or _____, from the days of slavery are on display at the museum.

5. Many monuments honor those who helped bring _____ to other people.

B. Write new sentences for all of the vocabulary words used above. Then underline the vocabulary word.

1. _____

   _____

2. _____

   _____

3. _____

   _____

4. _____

   _____

5. _____

   _____

Name _____

The **main idea** is the major, or most important, point of a story.
The **supporting details** are facts and information that reinforce the
main idea. When you summarize a story, you briefly tell the main
idea and at least one strong supporting detail in your own words.

**A. Read the paragraphs below. Then write the main idea and one
detail on the lines provided.**

Maya Lin is an architect who has designed several important monuments
and memorials in the United States. She has a special talent for creating
spaces that touch people's emotions. Lin's works honor people who were part
of history.

Lin's Vietnam Veterans Memorial Wall has become the most visited
monument in Washington, D.C. The memorial is a large black granite wall
with names carved into the stone. Not everyone liked the memorial at first.
However, it eventually helped many veterans and their families by honoring
those who served.

Main idea: _____

_____

Detail: _____

_____

_____

**B. Now summarize the entire passage. Use the main idea and
details of the paragraphs in your summary.**

Summary: _____

_____

_____

_____

_____

At Home: Read a book, magazine, or newspaper. Take
turns finding the main idea and details in the paragraphs or
stories that you read.

As you read "Maya Lin: Architect of Memory," fill in the Main Idea Web.

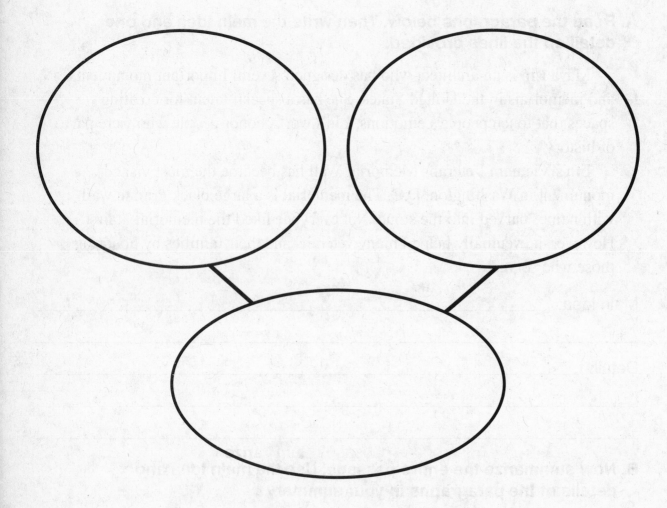

How does the information you wrote in this Main Idea Web help you
summarize "Maya Lin: Architect of Memory"?

At Home: Have the student use the chart to retell the story.

Name _____

As I read, I will pay attention to pronunciation.

	Why did so many people leave their homes? Why did they
11	leave behind everything they knew? Why did they risk their
21	lives and their families' lives to come to the United States?
32	Many were escaping hunger, poverty, or religious and
40	political persecution. The United States was their land of
49	hope. Many thought the streets were paved with gold. That's
59	why Ellis Island is called the "Golden Doors." Today's Ellis
69	Island is a museum honoring this important part of our
79	history.
80	To most immigrants, the United States was the land of
90	opportunity. It was a place where **equality** for all was
100	possible. To get there people saved everything they earned to
110	buy a ticket on a ship. Some came alone and bid their
122	families farewell forever. Others saved enough to bring their
131	families. For most immigrants the preparation and the
139	journey were not easy. 143

Comprehension Check

1. What is the main idea of this passage? **Summarize**

2. What are some reasons immigrants came to America? **Main Idea and Details**

	Words Read	–	Number of Errors	=	Words Correct Score
First Read		–		=	
Second Read		–		=	

At Home: Help the student read the passage, paying attention to the goal at the top of the page.

The **Internet** offers many online resources for research. Search engines are tools that enable you to search the Internet for information about a subject. You can use key words in a search engine to find information.

Use the Internet entries below to answer the questions.

1. Castle Clinton National Monument (National Park Service)
   Write to 26 Wall Street, New York, NY 10005.
   www.nps.gov/cacl/
2. The Immigration Experience
   Castle Garden, also known as Castle Clinton, was New York's first official immigration center. www.nyc.gov/html/nyc100/html/imm_stories/museum/
3. Clinton Castle—NY Military Museum and Veterans Research Center
   Castle Clinton was one of more than a dozen forts built to defend New York Harbor.
   www.dmna.state.ny.us/forts/fortsA_D/clintonCastle.htm

1. What would be key words to use in a search engine to find information

   about this place? _____

   _____

2. Which Web site could you visit to learn about the military history of Castle

   Clinton? _____

   _____

   _____

3. Which Web site could you visit to learn about immigrants who went through

   Castle Clinton? _____

   _____

4. Which Web site could you visit to learn when Castle Clinton became a

   national monument? _____

   _____

© Macmillan/McGraw-Hill

At Home: Together with a family member or helper, use key words in a search engine to find a Web site about a monument and write a short paragraph about it.

You can change the form of a word by adding a suffix such as **-ed** or **-ing.** This will create **inflected endings.** The inflected ending **-ed** is added to a verb to show that something happened in the past. The inflected ending **-ing** is added to a verb to show that something is happening in the present.

Remember these spelling rules:

1. If the base word ends with a consonant, double the final consonant before adding **-ed** or **-ing.**
2. If the base word ends in **y,** change the **y** to **i** before adding **-ed.**
3. If the base word ends in silent **e,** drop the **e** before adding **-ed** or **-ing.**

Add inflected endings to the words in parentheses, and write the new words on the lines.

Our family is (take) _____ a vacation in Washington, D.C.

As I research the city, I am (list) _____ how many sites

there are to visit. I am (plan) _____ to see many monuments

and memorials. (See) _____ the Lincoln Memorial is

an exciting thought. I am going (jog) _____ past the

Washington Monument. There are new places to visit, such as the National

Museum of the American Indian. I (ask) _____ my best

friend for her ideas about fascinating places to go. She said that I should

see the Vietnam Veterans Memorial Wall. Apparently, many people (cry)

_____ when they visited the Vietnam Veterans Memorial

Wall. I have (log) _____ all my research notes in a journal

that I will take on our trip.

© Macmillan/McGraw-Hill

At Home: Make a three-column chart with five verbs and inflected endings.

An **inflected ending** is an ending that is added to a word to show a change in the way the word is used. When you add an inflected ending, follow the spelling rules shown in the examples below to keep the vowel sound of the base word the same. Add **-ing** for present tense and **-ed** for past tense.

Examples:

hope + **-ing** = hoping   Drop the silent **e** so that **hope** keeps a long **o** sound.

hop + **-ing** = hopping   Double the end consonant so that **hop** keeps a short **o** sound.

deny + **-ed** = denied   Change the **y** to **i** so that deny keeps a long **e** sound and the long **i** sound of **y**.

Say the words below aloud. Add the best inflected endings from the box to the base words. Write the new word on the line using the spelling rules. Use the tense in parentheses to help you.

-ing	-ed

1. drip (present)   + _____ = _____

2. amuse (present)   + _____ = _____

3. jog (present)   + _____ = _____

4. qualify (past)   + _____ = _____

5. rake (present)   + _____ = _____

6. rely (past)   + _____ = _____

7. forbid (present)   + _____ = _____

8. ease (present)   + _____ = _____

9. apply (past)   + _____ = _____

10. regret (past)   + _____ = _____

© Macmillan/McGraw-Hill

At Home: Together with a family member or helper, read a newspaper to find five more words with inflected endings. Write a sentence for each word.

A. From the box, choose a vocabulary word with a meaning similar to the underlined word or words in each sentence. Write the vocabulary word on the line provided.

forbidden	reluctant	mischievous	hesitation
blared	gossiped	elegant	irresistible

1. Without <u>a pause</u>, I agreed to travel with my mother to Puerto Rico.

   _____

2. I was <u>unwilling</u> to give up another day of the trip. _____

3. I <u>talked casually</u> with friends about my aunts and uncles in Puerto Rico.

   _____

4. The loudspeaker <u>boomed loudly</u> when it announced our flight.

   _____

5. The woman's <u>tasteful, stylish</u> outfit caught our attention.

   _____

6. The urge to talk to her was <u>impossible to ignore</u>. _____

7. I tried to keep quiet because talking to strangers was <u>not allowed</u>.

   _____

8. The <u>naughty</u> children made faces at the people walking past.

   _____

B. Write new sentences for two of the vocabulary words used above. Then underline the vocabulary word.

9. _____

   _____

10. _____

    _____

Characters will often face a problem throughout a story. His or her efforts to solve this problem make up the plot. By recognizing the **problem and solution** you will be able to summarize the entire story.

Read the story below. Then complete the story chart.

We were flying to the Dominican Republic to visit my father's family, and I was anxious. I had never been on a plane before. When the plane was about to take off, my brother told me to close my eyes and picture myself on a beach. Soon I was lying in the sun and watching the palm trees. By the time I opened my eyes, the plane had already taken off and we were cruising smoothly.

When we arrived, we headed straight for the beach. Soon, my cousins wanted to go in the water. Unfortunately, I didn't know how to swim. One of my cousins had brought an inflatable tube. Carefully, I waded out to where they were swimming and floated safely in the tube.

The next day, my cousins went snorkeling. Because I couldn't swim, I was used to being in shallow water. I was afraid to go into deeper water. But after hearing my cousins talk about the amazing fish and coral reefs, I decided I wanted to go, too. I asked my father to float on a raft with me. He sat in the raft, close to where we snorkeled. I wore a life jacket to keep me on the surface of the water. We swam all day. It was wonderful!

Fill in the three solutions that match the problems below.

Problem	Solution
1. The narrator is nervous about flying.	_____ _____
2. The narrator doesn't know how to swim.	_____ _____
3. The narrator is afraid to go into deeper water.	_____ _____

At Home: Use the table to write a summary of the story. When you have finished, read your summary aloud to a family member or helper.

As you read *The Night of San Juan,* fill in the Story Map.

Character

Setting

Problem

Events

Solution

How does the information you wrote in the Story Map help you summarize *The Night of San Juan*?

 At Home: Have the student use the chart to retell the story.

As I read, I will pay attention to pauses and intonation.

	Soledad would roll out of bed each and every morning,
10	even before the rooster started crowing. She would grab her
20	backpack. Then she'd give her grandfather Sebastián a goodbye
29	kiss and set off on a one-hour march down a dusty road.
41	Soledad took the same road to school each day. She always
52	found something new along the way. Sometimes it was the way
63	the sun sparkled on some bright green leaves. Another time it
74	might be a bird singing a song.
81	Some days the walk to school seemed to take forever. The
92	hot sun would beat down on Soledad and the dusty road. So
104	she would stop to rest under a *ceiba* (SAY-bah) tree. She loved
116	observing everything around her. A short distance away, Soledad
125	might spot a pair of **mischievous** lizards chasing each other in
136	circles at the edge of the dirt road. 144

Comprehension Check

1. How would you describe Soledad? **Character**

2. What does the word mischievous mean? **Vocabulary**

	Words Read	–	Number of Errors	=	Words Correct Score
First Read		–		=	
Second Read		–		=	

At Home: Help the student read the passage, paying attention to the goal at the top of the page.

Name _____

An almanac is a reference book that is published each year.
Almanac entries have **charts** that provide brief facts and statistics
about a topic. Charts are a good place to find information on
history, geography, and government.

**Look at the incomplete chart on Puerto Rico. Match each piece of
information with the correct heading. Write the letter of your answer
on the correct line.**

Commonwealth of Puerto Rico

1. **Population (2003):** _____

2. **Official languages:** _____

3. **Total land area:** _____

4. **Capital:** _____

5. **Flower:** _____

6. **Climate:** _____

a. Flor de maga (Puerto Rican hibiscus)

b. Spanish and English

c. San Juan

d. 3,425 square miles

e. 3,885,877

f. Mild, with an average temperature of 77° F

© Macmillan/McGraw-Hill

At Home: With the help of a family member or helper, think
of three more facts that you would like to know about Puerto
Rico that are not listed in the above chart.

Suffixes are word parts added to the ends of base words to change their meanings or their parts of speech.

- The suffix *-ity* means "the state of." For example, when you add the suffix *-ity* to **visible,** the word **visibility** means "the state of being visible."
- The suffix *-ion* means "act or process." When you add *-ion* to **demonstrate,** the word **demonstration** means "the act of demonstrating."
- The suffix *-ous* means "having the qualities of." For example, when you add *-ous* to the word **poison,** the word **poisonous** means "having the qualities of poison."

In each sentence, underline the word that includes the suffix *-ity, -ion,* or *-ous.* Then write each word and its meaning. Remember that there may be spelling changes when you add the suffix.

1. The mischievous girl liked to play tricks on her sisters.

   _____

2. Amalia has the ability to make friends easily.

   _____

3. With no hesitation, the boy loudly declared, "I want to go, too!"

   _____

4. Juan was suspicious of his younger brother when the last cookie disappeared.

   _____

5. Our Spanish teacher always makes us work on our pronunciation.

   _____

© Macmillan/McGraw-Hill

At Home: Write three sentences about a trip, using words that end in *-ity, -ion,* or *-ous.*

- The **/ô/** sound can be spelled *aw,* as in l**aw**, or *au,* as in h**au**l, or *ough,* as in b**ough**t.
- The **/ou/** sound can be spelled *ou,* as in c**ou**nter, or *ow,* as in c**ow**.
- The **/oi/** sound can be spelled *oi,* as in b**oi**l, or *oy,* as in l**oy**al.

Write the words below in the correct column according to their vowel sounds. Remember that different letters can make the same vowel sounds. Circle the letters in each word that make the /ô/, /ou/, or /oi/ vowel sound.

dawdle	brought	crowd	toil	sought
joint	loyal	noise	mountain	loud
daughter	fountain	sprawls	foil	point
house	thought	bawl	royal	mouse

/ô/ sound, as in *law*	/ou/ sound, as in *now*	/oi/ sound, as in *boy*
1. _____	1. _____	1. _____
2. _____	2. _____	2. _____
3. _____	3. _____	3. _____
4. _____	4. _____	4. _____
5. _____	5. _____	5. _____
6. _____	6. _____	6. _____
7. _____	7. _____	7. _____

At Home: Together with a family member or helper, find one more word for each column of the chart.

A. Select the correct vocabulary word from the choices in parentheses. Write the word on the line provided.

1. Horses were important to the cowboy's job. They enabled the cowboy to travel easily over the (vastness, horizon) of the countryside.

   _____

2. The cowboys had great (hunger, enthusiasm) for their job and eagerly helped the rancher herd the cattle. _____

3. Sometimes it seemed as though the horses could ride all the way to the (horizon, vastness), where the land met the sky. _____

4. The (vastness, presence) of the horses helped keep the cattle under control. _____

5. Both cows and horses had to be careful not to slip into a (horizon, ravine). Such a steep, narrow canyon was a danger. _____

6. Horses (suspended, swerved) around the cows to keep the herd moving in the right direction. _____

7. The cowboys and their horses relaxed as the campfire (flickered, swerved) and flashed. _____

8. The horses slept with the cowboys' spurs (flickered, suspended) from the top of their saddles. _____

B. Write new sentences for two of the vocabulary words used above. Then underline the vocabulary word.

9. _____

   _____

10. _____

   _____

Name _____

When you use clues in the text to figure out what is not stated directly, you **make inferences.** Making inferences involves making logical guesses and using knowledge that you already have. When you make an inference, or "read between the lines," you fill in details that are not described directly. After you have made inferences, you can analyze the story and its characters.

Read each passage, then make an inference about the situations and characters.

1. Bob Lemmons saw the wild mustangs and pulled the reins to slow his horse, Warrior. The mustangs looked up but didn't run.
Inference: Bob slowed his horse because

_____

2. Bob was the only cowboy who could get close to the wild horses. They accepted him into the herd.
Inference: Bob's relationship with horses was

_____

3. The sky darkened, and Bob saw lightning flash around him. He quickly led Warrior to a ravine for shelter.
Inference: Bob and Warrior sought shelter because

_____

4. The mustang stallion fought Bob and Warrior. Bob guided Warrior's blows and the stallion fell, returning meekly to the herd.
Inference: The leaders of the mustang herd after the fight are

_____

5. **Analyze your inferences. What do they tell you about Bob's life as a cowboy?** _____

_____

_____

At Home: Using a short newspaper article, work with a family member or helper to make inferences about the piece.

Black Cowboy Wild Horses
Grade 5/Unit 2

67

© Macmillan/McGraw-Hill

As you read *Black Cowboy, Wild Horses,* fill in the Inferences Chart.

Text Clues	What You Know	Inferences

How does the information you wrote in the Inferences Chart help you monitor comprehension of *Black Cowboy, Wild Horses*?

At Home: Have the student use the chart to retell the story.

Practice

Fluency

As I read, I will pay attention to expression, phrasing, and tempo.

	Alice was born in 1902 on a ranch near Red Lodge,
11	Montana. Because they traveled on horses, the Greenough
19	family kept dozens of them to ride. Alice also fed cattle,
30	roped them, and rounded them up. She developed the riding
40	and roping skills that would later bring her fame.
49	Alice had seven brothers and sisters, five of whom wound
59	up working in rodeos. They became known as the "Riding
69	Greenoughs." Alice later said, "We learned to ride before we
79	could walk."
81	Ranch life was busy. The family planted, grew, and
90	harvested crops. Cattle had to be rounded up and fed.
100	Someone had to tame the horses and teach them to carry a
112	rider or pull a wagon. In addition, the fences needed fixing,
123	and the buildings and machines needed repairs. 130

Comprehension Check

1. What were some of the chores on the Greenoughs' ranch? **Summarize**

2. Why do you think five of the Greenoughs ended up working in rodeos?
Draw Conclusions

	Words Read	–	Number of Errors	=	Words Correct Score
First Read		–		=	
Second Read		–		=	

At Home: Help the student read the passage, paying
attention to the goal at the top of the page.

When you read poetry, pay attention to features often used with poetic language. For example, poems often include **repetition,** which occurs when a line or a sequence of lines appears more than once. **Assonance** is the repetition of the same or similar vowel sounds in a series of words, usually words with different consonant sounds. Repetition and assonance give poems a musical quality and rhythm.

Read the poem. Then answer the questions.

1 There once was a filly named Blaze,
2 Who wouldn't come out of the rain.
3 First that filly got soaked.
4 Then she grew hoarse and croaked,
5 Which put out that filly named Blaze.

1. In which lines do you see repetition? _____
   _____

2. What is the example of assonance in the repeated words? _____
   _____

3. What other examples of assonance do you see in line 1? _____
   _____

4. What is the example of assonance in line 2? _____
   _____

5. Is there an example of assonance in line 3? _____
   _____

6. Is there an example of assonance in line 4? _____
   _____

At Home: Together with a family member or helper, write out the words to another poem. Underline words and lines that are repeated. Then circle examples of assonance.

An analogy is a statement that compares two pairs of words. The relationship between the two words in the first pair is the same as the relationship between the two words in the second pair. **Antonyms,** two words with opposite meanings, can be used in analogies.

| criticize | cry | energetic | absence | soft |

Complete each analogy by providing an appropriate antonym from the box. Then write one sentence using one pair of words.

1. feebly is to strongly as tired is to _____

_____

_____

2. presence is to _____ as arrive is to depart

_____

_____

3. light is to heavy as _____ is to hard

_____

_____

4. awake is to sleep as praise is to _____

_____

_____

5. laugh is to _____ as smile is to frown

_____

_____

At Home: Together with a family member or helper, write the first pair of words of an analogy containing antonyms. Then work together to write the second pair of words.

Black Cowboy Wild Horses
Grade 5/Unit 2

71

Some words contain a Vowel-Consonant-Consonant-Vowel (VCCV) pattern. The two consonants in the middle of the word may be the same. In the word **valley,** for example, the consonant **l** is repeated. In some words, such as **winter,** the consonants are different (**n** and **t**).

blizzard	mutter	pigment	stack	wall	gallop
champion	empire	worship	fifteen	truck	

A. Identify the words that have a VCCV spelling pattern. Then write them on the lines.

_____

_____

B. Sort the words you chose into columns according to whether they have two consonants that are the same or two consonants that are different in their VCCV pattern.

Words with the Same Consonants

_____

_____

_____

_____

Words with Different Consonants

_____

_____

_____

_____

C. Complete each word by choosing the correct pair of letters. Then write the letters on the line.

1. ho _____ ow   (ll   gh)

2. fla _____ er   (gm   tt)

3. de _____ ist   (nt   pp)

At Home: Together with a family member or helper, write five more VCCV words. Write the words on index cards. Take turns identifying the vowels and consonants in the words.

© Macmillan/McGraw-Hill

A. Read each word in the first column. Find its synonym, or the word closest in meaning, in the second column. Then write the letter of the word on the line.

Column 1   Column 2

_____ **1.** shrieks   **a.** devoted

_____ **2.** predators   **b.** displays

_____ **3.** exhibits   **c.** screams

_____ **4.** mischievous   **d.** canyon

_____ **5.** ravine   **e.** naughty

_____ **6.** dedicated   **f.** hunters

reluctant   mournful   gossiped   presence   equality

B. Choose the word from the box above that best completes each sentence.

1. The women _____ about what had taken place the night before.

2. At first, Mom and Dad were _____ to have a dog stay in the house.

3. The _____ of humans frightened the wild animals.

4. The people's faces at the war memorial were _____.

5. There was a small plaque explaining that the soldiers had fought for _____.

A. Read each question. Then write your answer, using complete sentences, on the line provided.

1. What does it mean to alert?

_____

2. If the lights flickered, what did they do?

_____

3. When is something irresistible?

_____

4. What are artifacts, and where might you find them?

_____

5. What is an example of something that vibrates?

_____

6. What does it mean to slurp a bowl of soup?

_____

B. Write a definition for each of the following words.

1. delivering

_____

2. survive

_____

3. elegant

_____

4. suspended

_____

5. blared

_____

Complete each sentence by choosing the best word from the box.

swagger	navigation	patriots	tyrant
governor	spunk	stark	instruct

1. All of the proud British soldiers marched with a _____ as they approached the town.

2. Paul Revere and others were great American _____ who loved their country and warned the colonists of British attacks.

3. The American colonists needed someone with _____ to lead the revolution.

4. The _____ of the *Somerset*, a British ship, was not an easy task, especially in the dangerous seas.

5. Many American colonists believed that they were being treated cruelly

   by a _____.

6. A _____ helped keep order and enforce the laws in the American colonies.

7. The landscape was _____ on the night of Paul Revere's famous midnight ride.

8. Paul Revere tried to _____ the colonists to prepare for war.

Name _____

Authors don't always tell you everything directly in the story. Sometimes you have to make inferences and **draw conclusions** about a selection or character by using clues from the text along with your own experiences. Drawing conclusions will help you understand the selection better.

Read the following lines from "The Midnight Ride of Paul Revere." Then answer the questions.

You know the rest in the books you have read
How the British Regulars fired and fled,
How the farmers gave them ball for ball,
From behind each fence and the farmyard wall,
Chasing the red-coats down the lane,
Then crossing the fields to emerge again
Under the trees at the turn of the road,
And only pausing to fire and load.

1. What conclusion can you make about the colonists fighting the British Regulars? What evidence supports your conclusion?

_____

_____

_____

_____

2. Did the British retreat? What line(s) from the poem support your conclusion?

_____

3. How do you know that the colonists were determined to gain their independence? What was the result of their fight for freedom?

_____

_____

_____

At Home: Write a summary that draws a conclusion from a book or news article about the American Revolution.

Name _____

As you read *Sleds on Boston Common,* fill in the Conclusions Chart.

Text Clues	Conclusion

How does the information you wrote in the Conclusions Chart help you make inferences and analyze *Sleds on Boston Common*?

At Home: Have the student use the chart to retell the story.

Name _____

As I read, I will pay attention to pauses.

	Life in the colonies was changing. Roads had been built
10	connecting the cities. The colonies were trading with one
19	another more. People and ideas were moving along with
28	goods. These changes had made the ties among the colonists
38	stronger. They were beginning to feel more American
46	than British.
48	Then, in 1765, the British passed the Stamp Act. It was
58	one of the taxes that the British were using to help pay for
71	their war with France.
75	The colonists were furious. It wasn't only the money,
84	although times were hard. They were angry because they
93	hadn't voted for this tax. The colonists believed that only
103	representatives whom they chose could ask them to pay
112	taxes. The colonists said there could be "no taxation without
122	representation."
123	And so the first step toward the American Revolution
132	began over a fight about taxes.
138	Colonists refused to pay the stamp tax. Some people
147	boycotted, or refused to buy, British goods or enter any store
158	that carried British goods. 162

Comprehension Check

1. What caused the colonists to feel more American than British? **Cause and Effect**

2. Why were colonists so angry about the stamp tax? **Main Idea and Details**

	Words Read	–	Number of Errors	=	Words Correct Score
First Read		–		=	
Second Read		–		=	

Sleds on Boston Common
Grade 5/Unit 3

At Home: Help the student read the passage, paying attention to the goal at the top of the page.

Narrative poetry is poetry that tells a story or gives an account of events. **Meter** is the regular arrangement of accented and unaccented syllables in a line of poetry. **Alliteration** is the repetition of the same first letter or sound in a series of words.

A. Read the passage from the poem. Mark the meter of each line by separating the syllables with a slash. Then underline the accented syllables. Then answer the questions.

> Meanwhile, his friend, through alley and street,
> Wanders and watches, with eager ears,
> Till in the silence around him he hears
> The muster of men at the barrack door,
> And the measured tread of the grenadiers,
> Marching down to their boats on the shore.

1. Based on this passage, how do you know the poem is narrative poetry?

_____

_____

_____

2. Which lines use alliteration? Give examples.

_____

_____

_____

B. Rewrite the following line so that it uses alliteration.

3. Marching down to their boats on the shore.

_____

At Home: Write your own poem about the American Revolution using alliteration and meter.

Sleds on Boston Common
Grade 5/Unit 3

79

Name _____

Many long words have smaller root words within them. With
many words it is easy to **build word families** by adding
a suffix or a prefix.

**A. For the words listed below, write an additional word that is part
of the same word family.**

1. patriot

   unpatriotic _____

2. tyrant

   tyrannical _____

3. navigate

   navigation _____

4. govern

   governor _____

**B. Complete the sentence by using the correct word from the word
families above.**

5. The American colonists created their own _____.

6. A person who is not loyal to his or her country is said to be

   _____.

7. Paul Revere showed great _____ for the American colonies
   during his midnight ride.

8. The _____ of the *Somerset*, a British ship, had to have
   good eyesight.

At Home: Read a magazine article and find two words that
have word families. Then write the different word families on
a sheet of paper, and read them to a family member or helper.

Name _____

The point at which two syllables meet determines whether the vowel sound is long or short. If the syllable ends in a vowel, as in the word **hu-man**, then the vowel sound is long and has a **V/CV pattern**. If the syllable ends in a consonant, then the vowel sound is short and has a **VC/V pattern**, as in **wag-on**.

Say the words below and break them into syllables. Then write the word in syllables on the lines provided. Write *long* if the word has a V/CV pattern. Write *short* if the word has a VC/V pattern.

1. humor _____ _____

2. pilot _____ _____

3. lemon _____ _____

4. punish _____ _____

5. lazy _____ _____

6. legal _____ _____

7. comet _____ _____

8. profile _____ _____

9. frozen _____ _____

10. proper _____ _____

11. waken _____ _____

12. tuna _____ _____

At Home: Make an eight-column chart. Then sort the words above by vowel sound.

Name _____

**Choose a vocabulary word from the choices in parentheses.
Then write the correct word on the line provided.**

1. I will write a letter to my (representative/attorney) in Congress about this

   problem. _____

2. (Colonel/Physician) is one of the highest ranks among the officers in the

   army. _____

3. Before Christina Smith was elected to Congress, she was a representative

   in the state (legislature/suffrage). _____

4. To (submit/qualify) as a voter, you must be at least eighteen years old.

   _____

5. Congress is still debating, so they will delay, or (submit/postpone), the vote

   until next week. _____

6. She knew that the old law was not (satisfactory/escorted) for today.

   _____

7. When we finish writing, we can (submit/qualify) our letters to our

   representatives. _____

8. Our (attorney/physician) will present our case to the judge.

   _____

A **fact** is a statement that can be proven true. An **opinion** is a statement that a person believes, but that cannot be proven true.

Use information from "When Esther Morris Headed West," to decide whether each statement below is a fact or an opinion. Write your choice in the box next to each sentence. Then explain each of your decisions.

Statement	Fact or Opinion	Explanation of Decision
Esther Morris was the smartest person in Wyoming.		
Benjamin Sheeks thought that women's suffrage was hogwash.		
In 1869 the Wyoming legislature voted to give women of Wyoming the vote.		
The people who lived in Wyoming in 1869 were pleasant.		
Esther ran for office after women in Wyoming got the vote.		
After Esther Morris was elected, people felt the happiest they ever had about the government.		

© Macmillan/McGraw-Hill

At Home: Write three sentences that are facts and three sentences that are opinions.

When Esther Morris Headed West
Grade 5/Unit 3

83

Name _____

As you read *When Esther Morris Headed West,* fill in the
Fact and Opinion Chart.

Fact	Opinion

How does the information you wrote in the Fact and Opinion Chart help
you evaluate *When Esther Morris Headed West*?

At Home: Have the student use the chart to retell the story.

Name _____

As I read, I will pay attention to pronunciation.

	The fight for woman's rights started with the fight to end
11	slavery. Beginning in the 1820s, many women became active
19	in the struggle for the abolition (ab-uh-LISH-uhn), or end,
27	of slavery.
29	One woman who worked hard to fight slavery was
38	Lucretia Mott. In 1833 she started a women's antislavery
46	society in Philadelphia. She went to London to attend the
56	first World's Anti-Slavery Convention. Women had to sit
64	behind a curtain. They couldn't be seen or heard. Lucretia
74	Mott was furious.
77	Also attending the London convention was Elizabeth
84	Cady Stanton. She, too, was angry at the limited role that
95	women were allowed. She and Mott became friends. Mott
104	was some 20 years older, but they shared many of the
114	same views.
116	The two friends began to talk with other women who
126	were working to free the slaves. They talked about how hard
137	women's lives were. They talked about the need to make
147	changes. They talked about how they might work together to
157	fight for their own rights. 162

Comprehension Check

1. What does the word abolition mean? **Context Clues**

2. How did Lucretia Mott fight to end slavery? **Main Idea and Details**

	Words Read	–	Number of Errors	=	Words Correct Score
First Read		–		=	
Second Read		–		=	

At Home: Help the student read the passage, paying attention to the goal at the top of the page.

When Esther Morris Headed West
Grade 5/Unit 3

85

© Macmillan/McGraw-Hill

A **time line** is a diagram of several events arranged in the order in which they took place. A time line helps to arrange information in an easy, visual way.

Important Events in the Women's Suffrage Movement

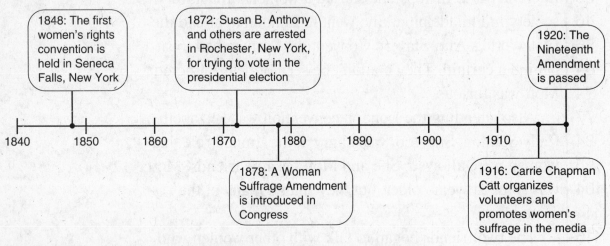

1848: The first women's rights convention is held in Seneca Falls, New York

1872: Susan B. Anthony and others are arrested in Rochester, New York, for trying to vote in the presidential election

1920: The Nineteenth Amendment is passed

1840 1850 1860 1870 1880 1890 1900 1910

1878: A Woman Suffrage Amendment is introduced in Congress

1916: Carrie Chapman Catt organizes volunteers and promotes women's suffrage in the media

Use the time line to answer the following questions:

1. What is this time line about? _____

   _____

2. How many years does the time line cover? _____

3. What happened in 1872? _____

   _____

4. Where was the first women's rights conference in the United States held?

   _____

5. Who traveled across America to organize volunteers?

   _____

6. Which happened first: Seneca Falls Convention or the Nineteenth

   Amendment is ratified? _____

At Home: With a family member or helper, write five important events and organize them on a time line.

Name _____

A dictionary tells you a word's meaning, and it includes a
pronunciation key that tells you how to say a word correctly.
Look at these symbols from a dictionary's pronunciation key:

Long vowel sounds have a line over the letter: ē as in *feed*; ā as in face.
Short vowel sounds use the letter itself: i as in *kid*; u as in *submit*.
The "oo" sound has one dot over *u: u̇* as in *book*.
The "ew" sound has two dots over *u: ü* as in *crew*.

Notice how words are spelled when pronunciation symbols are used:

fās = face   submit = submit
kid = kid   bu̇k = book
crü = crew

**Using pronunciation symbols for the vowel sounds, rewrite the
words below.**

Example: true _____trü_____

1. riot _____

2. postpone _____

3. five _____

4. made _____

5. took _____

6. sun _____

7. look _____

8. holiday _____

9. waist _____

10. frigid _____

At Home: Read the pronunciation key in a dictionary. Then
use pronunciation symbols to write three words.

Some words have a pattern with a syllable break between two vowels. This is called the **V/V pattern**. The word *fuel*, for example, has a syllable break between the vowel **u** and the vowel **e**. This pattern is also found in words with more than two syllables, such as the word *idea*, which has a syllable break between the vowel **e** and the vowel **a**.

Underline the words below that have a V/V pattern. Then draw a line between the two vowels in each underlined word to show where the V/V pattern is found.

diary _____   fluid _____

piano _____   hoarse _____

minus _____   diameter _____

meteor _____   ruin _____

poet _____   patriot _____

riot _____   trial _____

valley _____   diet _____

casual _____   meander _____

about _____   cruel _____

rodeo _____   fought _____

closet _____   genuine _____

radio _____   without _____

At Home: Read a favorite book to find six more words that have the V/V pattern. List the words and then read them aloud.

© Macmillan/McGraw-Hill

Name _____

A. Choose the word from the list that best completes each sentence.

> humanity   inevitable   unheeded   enlightened   prevailing

1. It is _____ that the landfill will close because it is full.

2. The mayor's speech last year about the importance of recycling seems to

   have gone _____.

3. Many people believe that pollution is a _____ cause of Earth's extreme weather.

4. Scientists have become more _____ about the effects of pollution.

5. An improved environment would help all of _____.

B. Write a sentence for each vocabulary word.

6. _____.

   _____

7. _____

   _____

8. _____

   _____

9. _____

   _____

10. _____

    _____

A **fact** is something that can be proven true.
An **opinion** is a belief that cannot be proven true.

Read each sentence and decide whether it is a fact or an opinion.
Then circle *Fact* or *Opinion*.

1. People need to change their attitude toward the environment. Fact Opinion

2. The steam engine was invented during the Industrial Revolution. Fact Opinion

3. The ozone layer protects us from the sun's harmful rays. Fact Opinion

4. Fifth graders in Parma, Michigan, created Environmental Awareness Day. Fact Opinion

5. Scientists know that pollution is a main cause of global warming. Fact Opinion

6. Technology is the answer to all of the problems that we face. Fact Opinion

7. Recycling one ton of paper saves 17 trees and 7,000 gallons of water. Fact Opinion

8. Cities and towns will be clean and pleasant in the future. Fact Opinion

9. Acid rain can damage plants, animals, and even buildings. Fact Opinion

10. Paper is the best material to recycle. Fact Opinion

© Macmillan/McGraw-Hill

At Home: With a family member or helper, read a newspaper or a magazine and list five facts and five opinions.

Name _____

As you read "Beyond the Horizon", fill in the Fact and Opinion Chart.

Opinion	
Fact	

How does the information you wrote in this Fact and Opinion Chart help you evaluate "Beyond the Horizon"?

At Home: Have the student use the chart to retell the story.

As I read, I will pay attention to pauses.

	The U.S. is the third biggest country in the world. Its area
12	is 3,717,813 square miles.
15	We're doing a good job of filling all this space. Since
26	1900, the U.S. population has gone from 76 million people to
35	over 294 million in 2004. It's **inevitable** that our numbers
43	will grow.
45	As our country grows, people and animals sometimes
53	find that they share a neighborhood! Humans need more and
63	more space to live. They sometimes take land that wild
73	animals need for food or shelter. Many homes are now built
84	on the edge of forests. We build houses by lakes. Living
95	together is not easy for **humanity** or the animals. We must
106	learn to live together and to respect each other. We have to
118	learn to be good neighbors.
123	Today more and more of people live outside of cities. As
134	a result, our landscape is changing. Family farms are sold.
144	Forests are cleared. And houses are built on the land. 154

Comprehension Check

1. How is population growth affecting wild animals? **Main Idea and Details**

2. How is the landscape in the United States changing? **Main Ideas and Details**

	Words Read	–	Number of Errors	=	Words Correct Score
First Read		–		=	
Second Read		–		=	

© Macmillan/McGraw-Hill

At Home: Help the student read the passage, paying attention to the goal at the top of the page.

Using an outline can help you group facts and organize information while you study. First skim, or quickly read, the article. Next scan, or look carefully, for the titles, headings, and key vocabulary words of the article. Then write your notes in an outline.

Look at the outline below. Then answer the questions.

Environmental Dangers

I. Global warming

    A. Pollution is making it inevitable that ice at Earth's poles will melt.

    B. Coastlines and weather will change.

II. Damage to the ozone layer

    A. Ozone gas protects us from the sun.

    B. Pollution has caused the amount of ozone to decrease.

III. Acid rain

    A. Pollution from fossil fuels mixes with rain.

    B. Acid rain can harm trees, wildlife, and buildings.

1. What sort of information follows the Roman numerals? _____

_____

_____

2. What sort of information follows the capital letters? _____

_____

_____

© Macmillan/McGraw-Hill

At Home: Outline the summary of Kofi Annan's speech to world leaders about the health of the environment.

Name _____

A **prefix** is a word part that can be added to the beginning of a word to change the word's meaning. Knowing what a prefix means can help you learn what a word means. For example, the prefix *re-* means *again, anew,* or *back/backward*. The prefix *in-* can mean *within, into,* or *toward*. Both the prefix *in-* and the prefix *un-* can mean *not*.

Write the prefix of each word. Write the word's meaning. Then use the word in a sentence of your own.

Prefix	+	Word	=	New Word	Meaning
re	+	new	=	renew	to make new again
in	+	side	=	inside	on the inner side, within something

1. resend   Prefix: _____   Meaning: _____

Sentence: _____

2. unhappy   Prefix: _____   Meaning: _____

Sentence: _____

_____

3. review   Prefix: _____   Meaning: _____

Sentence: _____

_____

4. If the word **heeded** means "noticed," what does **unheeded** mean?

Prefix: _____   Meaning: _____

Sentence: _____

_____

At Home: Watch the news or listen to the radio for at least two words that begin with the prefixes *re-, in-,* and *un-*.

Words that follow a **vowel-consonant-consonant-consonant-vowel pattern (VCCCV)** usually have two syllables. To divide these words into syllables, look for consonant blends—pairs of letters that work together to make one sound. These blends include pairs of letters such as the *pl* and *gr* found in words like **complain** and **pilgrim**. You cannot separate the sounds in a consonant blend: com/plain and pil/grim.

Compound words often fall into the VCCCV pattern. The consonant blend may appear in either the first or the second syllable. Divide compound words into syllables between the two smaller words, for example, cock/pit and foot/print.

Draw a line in each word to show the syllable break. Then group the words according to how they break, VC/CCV or VCC/CV, in the chart.

endless	instant	pumpkin
orphan	reckless	kingdom
hilltop	handsome	halfway
concrete	district	complete
grassland	monster	control
landlord	bookshelf	children

VCC/CV	VC/CCV

At Home: Look for words with a VC/CCV or VCC/CV word pattern in a newspaper, book, or magazine.

Beyond the Horizon
Grade 5/Unit 3

95

© Macmillan/McGraw-Hill

Name _____

A. Choose the word from the box that best completes each sentence.

> gnarled   parched   landscape   scorching
> gushed   brimming   scrawny   progress

1. The plants and trees began to dry and shrink from the heat of the

   _____ sun.

2. The twisted, _____ branches of the old tree provided little shade for picnickers.

3. The desert hare was thin and _____ from lack of food.

4. The heat slowed the explorers _____ across the sand.

5. The summer sun made the land look _____ from the lack of water.

6. Water _____ from a broken irrigation hose, flooding the crops.

7. The rains transformed the dry, stark _____ into bright fields of green.

8. Soon the buckets were _____ with water from the heavy rain.

B. Choose two of the vocabulary words and write a new sentence for each.

9. _____

   _____

10. _____

   _____

Name _____

When you **compare** things, you point out how they are alike.
When you **contrast** things, you point out how they are different.

Read the paragraphs below. Then use information from the passage to fill in the Compare-and-Contrast chart.

Trees are among the oldest living things on Earth. The baobab is a deciduous tree, or a tree that loses its leaves. Baobabs have very wide trunks that can grow to a diameter of more than 45 feet around. The wood in the trunk is pulpy and holds water easily. Most species of baobab grow in the hot, dry climate of Africa, from South Africa to Sudan. Several species also grow in Australia. Many baobabs live for 1,000 years or more.

Like baobabs, most coast redwoods are very old. Unlike baobabs, however, coast redwoods grow tall rather than wide. Coast redwoods are coniferous, not deciduous, so they do not lose their leaves. One of the tallest known redwoods is about 367 feet tall and 600 years old. The wood of the coast redwood is soft, red, and resistant to disease. Coast redwoods grow in areas along the western coast of the United States. They thrive in the foggy, damp, mountainous areas near the Pacific Ocean.

Baobab	Both	Coast redwoods
Type of tree: _____		Type of tree: _____
Growth: _____		Growth: _____
Wood: _____		Wood: _____
Climate: _____		Climate: _____

© Macmillan/McGraw-Hill

At Home: Make a chart that compares and contrasts your favorite food with the favorite food of a family member or helper.

Name _____

As you read *My Great-Grandmother's Gourd*, fill in the Venn Diagrams.

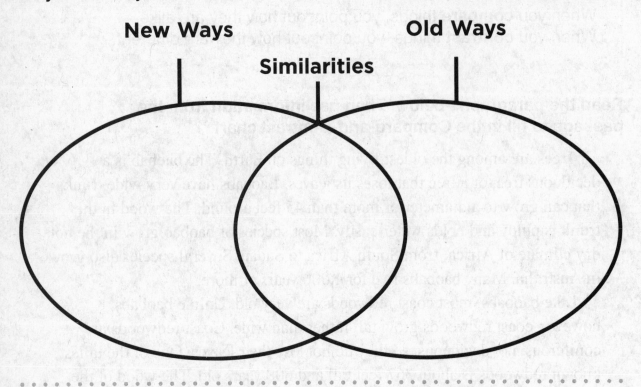

New Ways   Old Ways

Similarities

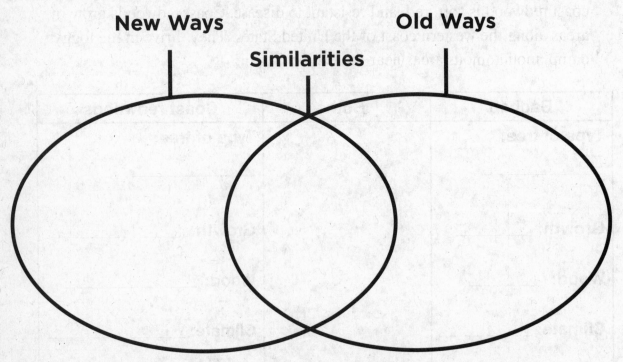

New Ways   Old Ways

Similarities

How does the information you wrote in the Venn Diagrams help you
make inferences and analyze *My Great-Grandmother's Gourd*?

© Macmillan/McGraw-Hill

At Home: Have the student use the chart to retell the story.

As I read, I will pay attention to tempo.

	The Mojave and Colorado deserts are two entirely
8	different ecosystems that exist side by side. Although they
17	are both arid, they look different, have different weather, and
27	are occupied by different living things.
33	These deserts are different because they are at two
42	different elevations, their height above sea level. The
50	Colorado Desert is below 3,000 feet in elevation. It has less
60	rainfall, fewer plants, and higher temperatures than the
68	Mojave Desert. The Mojave is over 3,000 feet in elevation.
77	It has more rainfall and temperatures can dip below freezing.
87	So Joshua Tree National Park contains two quite different
96	deserts. But the most remarkable thing about this park is
106	the area between the two deserts. This transition area is very
117	thin, generally less than a mile wide. In this slim zone,
128	animals and plants from both sides of the park are abundant.
139	But the cholla (CHOY-uh) cactus rules the zone. Don't walk
148	too close to this "jumping" cactus or the spiny needles will
159	snag you. Ouch! 162

Comprehension Check

1. Compare and contrast the Mojave and Colorado deserts. **Compare and Contrast**

2. What is the transition area? **Main Idea and Details**

	Words Read	–	Number of Errors	=	Words Correct Score
First Read		–		=	
Second Read		–		=	

© Macmillan/McGraw-Hill

At Home: Help the student read the passage paying attention to the goal at the top of the page.

Name _____

A **process diagram** is a drawing that shows how something is put together, how something works, or how something changes over time. In a diagram, the important parts of an object are labeled.

Below is a diagram of the water cycle. Use it to answer the questions.

2. Condensation: The water vapor rises, forms clouds, and is cooled by the air.

3. Precipitation: Water returns to Earth as rain, snow, or other precipitation. Some water seeps into the ground. Some water returns to the ocean.

1. Evaporation: The sun heats water in the soil, rivers, lakes, and oceans. The water evaporates and turns into water vapor, a gas.

1. What are two forms of precipitation? _____

2. What is the gas that results from evaporation called? _____

3. What does the water vapor form during condensation? _____

4. Where does water go when it falls back to Earth as precipitation?

_____

_____

5. What source of energy drives the water cycle? _____

6. What causes water to change from clouds into precipitation?

_____

_____

At Home: Find a process diagram in a magazine or newspaper. Then explain the diagram to a family member or helper.

© Macmillan/McGraw-Hill

The exact meaning of a word is called a **denotation**. Synonyms can carry positive or negative feelings, or **connotations**. For example, a thin person can be called *scrawny,* which has a negative connotation, or *lean,* which has a more positive connotation. Whether a word has a positive or a negative connotation often depends on a person's experience with the word. Some words are neutral and have no connotations.

Look at the chart below. For each neutral word, find a synonym that has either a negative or a positive connotation. You may use a thesaurus or dictionary for help to find words. Then write the word's exact meaning in the last column.

Neutral	Positive	Negative	Exact Meaning
smell		stink	
house	mansion		
filled	brimming		
unusual		strange	
plant		weed	
well-dressed		overdressed	
laugh	chuckle		
noise	music		

At Home: Look through a newspaper or magazine to find examples of advertisements that use words with positive or negative connotations.

Name _____

In words that have more than one syllable, one syllable is always stressed, or accented, more than the others. A stressed syllable can appear at the beginning or at the end of a two syllable word. The unaccented syllable often has the unaccented vowel sound /ə/. For example, the second syllable of the word *confirm* is accented. The first syllable has the /ə/ sound.

Look at each word below and circle the accented syllable. Then use a dictionary to check your work and write the pronunciation on the line provided.

1. helpful _____

2. control _____

3. common _____

4. loser _____

5. above _____

6. lentil _____

7. pronounce _____

8. golden _____

9. venom _____

10. layer _____

11. canal _____

12. perplex _____

13. welcome _____

14. salmon _____

15. provoke _____

16. tension _____

At Home: List five new words that have the /ə/ sound in the unaccented syllable. Use a dictionary to help you.

A. Label each sentence True if the boldface vocabulary word is used correctly. If a sentence is False, explain why on the line below.

1. A **defective** toy is in good working order. _____

   _____

2. If positions are **reversed** during a class debate, your team begins arguing

   for the opposite opinion. _____

   _____

3. A **meteor** comes from deep inside Earth. _____

   _____

4. A **robot** is a living thing. _____

   _____

5. If you see a tree branch that is **dangling**, it is lying on the ground. _____

   _____

6. My sister played with a spinning top that **rotated** in circles. _____

   _____

7. The tired runner **staggered** to the finish line, looking as if he might fall down.

   _____

8. You might use the **tokens** from a board game to buy lunch. _____

   _____

B. Choose two vocabulary words and use them in a sentence.

9. _____

   _____

10. _____

   _____

Authors don't always tell readers everything in a story, so you may have to draw your own conclusions. To **draw conclusions,** you rely on what you know from your own experience and combine it with clues from the story. Drawing conclusions as you read can help you better understand the story.

Read the two paragraphs below, then answer the questions.
Describe the clues that helped you draw a conclusion.

It was almost noon. Maria had been watching the clock for the last half hour. Wouldn't Mrs. Jones ever stop talking? Maria thought again of the green apple in her lunchbox. She could almost taste it. Then her stomach began to growl.

What conclusion can you draw about Maria? _____

_____

Story clues: _____

_____

Experience clues: _____

_____

Evan picked at his cereal. He knew he should have studied harder last night, but the dates all ran together in his head. Why did he have to learn American history anyway? For the third time, his mother told him to hurry. He put on his coat. He felt a sudden wave of dread.

What conclusion can you draw about Evan? _____

_____

Story clues: _____

_____

Experience clues: _____

_____

At Home: Write a short story with a beginning and middle, but no end. Then ask another person to read your story and draw conclusions about how the story could end.

Name _____

As you read Zathura, fill in the Conclusions Diagrams.

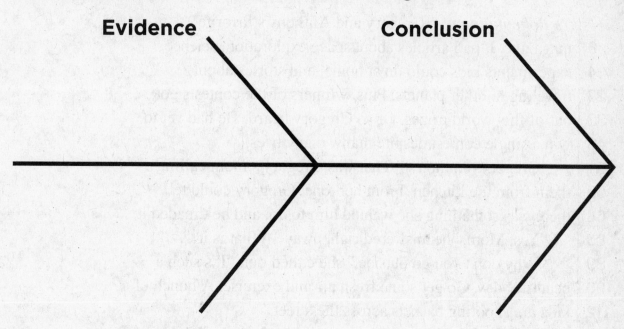

Evidence   Conclusion

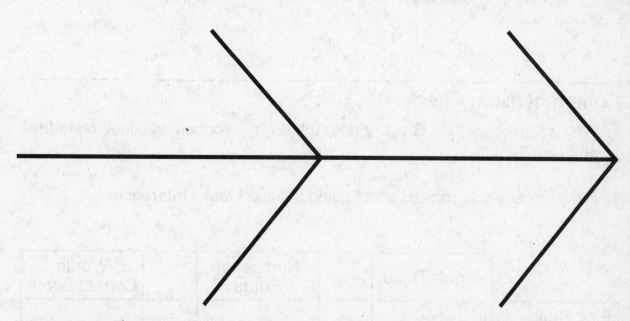

How does the information you wrote in the Conclusions Diagrams help
you make inferences and analyze Zathura?

At Home: Have the student use the chart to retell the story.

As I read, I will pay attention to punctuation.

	Robomation was Gregory and Anthony's favorite
6	magazine. It had articles about space exploration, science
14	experiments kids could do at home, and stories about
23	traveling to other planets. Plus, winners of the contests got
33	out-of-this-world prizes. Or so Gregory heard. He had yet to
43	win a single contest despite many, many tries.
51	"Gregory! Anthony!" That was Gregory's mom calling
58	them from the kitchen. From her tone, Gregory could tell
68	there was something she wanted him to do, and he dreaded it.
80	"Yes, Mom," he answered right away. "What is it?"
89	"Why don't you go outside," she called out. "It's such a
100	beautiful day. Go get some fresh air and exercise. A bunch of
112	kids are shooting baskets across the street."
119	Gregory knew his mother was talking about Jordan Veras
128	and the "cool" gang. Gregory didn't fit in with their group,
139	though he had tried often. Maybe, if he were someone else. . . .
150	"Okay, Mom," Gregory sighed. He knew his Mom was
159	right about the exercise. 163

Comprehension Check

1. Why was *Robomation* Gregory and Anthony's favorite magazine? **Main Idea and Details**

2. Why isn't Gregory excited about going outside? **Make Inferences**

	Words Read	–	Number of Errors	=	Words Correct Score
First Read		–		=	
Second Read		–		=	

At Home: Help the student read the passage, paying attention to the goal at the top of the page.

Newspaper articles tell about current events or trends. They answer the questions who, what, where, when, why, and how. A **headline** is a short title about an event or subject that is designed to grab the reader's attention. A **byline** tells who wrote the article.

Read the newspaper article below, then answer the questions.

Will Robots Replace Humans in Space?
by Rachel Ambrose
Dixon Daily Staff Writer

Will we ever have the same inspirational feelings for a robot that we had for Neil Armstrong or Sally Ride? No, but robots might soon be the astronauts of the future. The major advantage of using robots in space is that they do not need food, air, or rest. Robots can work 24 hours a day, seven days a week. They can carry out tasks that are too dangerous, difficult, or impossible for their human counterparts to do. Robots come in all different shapes and sizes. They can perform faster and with fewer errors than humans. Probably the most convincing reason for using robots in space is that they can be replaced, while human beings cannot.

1. What is the article about? _____

_____

2. Who wrote this article? _____

3. For which newspaper does the writer work? _____

4. Why is the headline important to this article? _____

_____

_____

5. Create a new headline for this article. _____

_____

At Home: Talk with a family member or helper about the information a newspaper article provides. Refer to the headline and byline by name.

An analogy is a comparison of two pairs of words. **Synonyms,** or words with the same meaning, can be used in analogies. The two words in the first pair match in the same way that the two words in the second pair match.

Read this example: Big is to large as thin is to ____slim____.

The words *big* and *large* are synonyms, and the words *thin* and *slim* are synonyms.

Complete each analogy by writing a synonym for the first word in the second pair of words.

1. Take is to grab as break is to _____.

2. Freedom is to liberty as talk is to _____.

3. Find is to discover as work is to _____.

4. Try is to attempt as shiver is to _____.

5. Car is to automobile as column is to _____.

6. Location is to place as choose is to _____.

7. Gift is to present as hole is to _____.

8. Country is to nation as ruler is to _____.

9. Drum is to instrument as friend is to _____.

10. Meal is to dinner as land is to _____.

At Home: Write a synonym for each of the following words: *ideas, cruel, gentler,* and *allow.* Then write an analogy for each pair of synonyms.

Name _____

The **schwa-r /ər/** sound is a vowel sound often found in unaccented syllables. The three most common spellings for words that end in the /ər/ sound include *ar, er,* and *or.*

A. Fill in the blanks with the correct ending sound: ar, er, or.

1. spid ___ ___

2. broth ___ ___

3. coll ___ ___

4. doll ___ ___

5. jogg ___ ___

6. schol ___ ___

7. err ___ ___

8. vap ___ ___

9. equat ___ ___

10. peddl ___ ___

11. barb ___ ___

12. generat ___ ___

B. Write a paragraph using at least six words from the list above. Make sure you underline each word.

_____

_____

_____

_____

_____

_____

_____

_____

_____

At Home: With a family member or helper, read a story and list all of the words that end with a /ər/ sound.

A. Match each description with the correct person in the box. Write your answer on the line next to the description.

patriots   governor   attorney   representative   defective

1. someone who practices law and represents people in court

   _____

2. people who love and support their country _____

3. an elected official who stands for the views of a certain group of people

   _____

4. the elected leader of a state or political body _____

5. having a flaw or weakness _____

B. Complete each sentence with a word from the box.

inevitable   gushed   prevailing   swagger   gnarled

6. It was once a _____ belief that certain natural resources would last forever.

7. The _____ branches of the ancient tree twisted up into the sky.

8. The proud soldier strode past with a _____ in his step.

9. Unless people work to stop pollution, damage to Earth's environment is

   _____.

10. As the snow melted, water ran into the streams and _____ down the mountain.

© Macmillan/McGraw-Hill

A. Match each word on the left with its antonym on the right. Write the letter of your answer on the line.

1. _____ enlightened   **a.** wet

2. _____ scrawny   **b.** moved forward

3. _____ parched   **c.** ignorant

4. _____ reversed   **d.** plump

B. On the lines provided, write a synonym from the words in the box for each word below. Then write a sentence for that word.

| bare | ignored | delay | burning | acceptable | turned |

5. stark _____

_____

6. postpone _____

_____

_____

7. satisfactory _____

_____

_____

8. unheeded _____

_____

_____

9. rotated _____

_____

10. scorching _____

_____

Name _____

A. Match the vocabulary word with its definition. Then write the correct word on the line.

blurted	permission	scald	autograph
fare	spectacular	clenched	chiseled

1. sensational, fantastic _____

2. burn _____

3. spoke suddenly _____

4. carved _____

5. closed together tightly _____

6. consent _____

7. a person's signed name _____

8. price charged for public transportation _____

B. Write a paragraph using at least three vocabulary words. Underline each vocabulary word you use.

_____

_____

_____

_____

_____

_____

_____

_____

_____

_____

When you summarize a story, you briefly retell it in your own words. You can describe the **characters** (people in the story) and **setting** (place where the story happens) in a summary.

Read this story, and then summarize it. Include information about the characters and setting.

'Tricia Ann listened carefully to her grandmother, Mama Frances. Everyone listened carefully to Mama Frances because the old woman was wise, strong, and had a no-nonsense attitude. She also had a huge heart.

" 'Tricia Ann," Mama Frances said, "it's your first trip alone downtown. Don't let anyone give you what-for, you hear? You keep going to Someplace Special with your head held high." Mama Frances was determined to boost her granddaughter's pride and self-confidence.

'Tricia Ann walked through the city. She saw sign after sign proclaiming Whites Only and Colored Section. White people glared at her as she passed them on the sidewalk. She wanted to run home crying. But 'Tricia Ann held her head high and walked bravely through the city streets.

Finally, she was there! 'Tricia Ann climbed the steps to the public library, her very own special place, where everyone was welcome. She knew that Mama Frances was right: March proudly, and you will get to where you want to go.

Summary: _____

_____

_____

_____

_____

_____

_____

_____

At Home: Read a story and identify the characters and setting.

Goin' Someplace Special
Grade 5/Unit 4

113

As you read *Goin' Someplace Special,* fill in the Character and
Setting Chart.

Character	Setting

How does the information you wrote in the Character and Setting Chart
help you analyze the story structure of *Goin' Someplace Special*?

_____

At Home: Have the student use the chart to retell the story.

As I read, I will pay attention to punctuation.

8	Josie and Franklin had heard Gramma's stories many times, but they never got tired of them. There was something
19	so comforting about Gramma's voice. Josie felt like she was
29	being wrapped in a warm, fuzzy blanket when she listened to
40	Gramma's stories. And even though Franklin was 14 going
48	on 15, he still liked to hear Gramma's stories about her life in
60	the South.
62	Now Franklin got up from the step where he had been
73	sitting. "Gramma, I have to go do my math homework. I'll
84	see you at dinner."
88	Josie stayed where she was. Like Gramma, Josie loved
97	nature, but living in the city didn't provide much. She looked
108	around the neighborhood. Outside their second-floor
114	apartment, Gramma had planted window boxes, bright with
122	red and white geraniums. Other than that a few spindly trees
133	that grew between the sidewalk and the curb were the only
144	green, growing things that Josie could see.
151	Other neighbors were sitting on their front stoops, too,
160	hoping for a cool evening breeze. 166

Comprehension Check

1. Why does Josie enjoy listening to Gramma's stories? **Make Inferences**

2. What do Josie and her grandmother have in common? **Main Idea and Details**

	Words Read	−	Number of Errors	=	Words Correct Score
First Read		−		=	
Second Read		−		=	

At Home: Help the student read the passage, paying attention to the goal at the top of the page.

A **time line** is a diagram that organizes information. Time lines help you keep track of events in the order in which they took place.

Look at the time line. Then answer the questions.

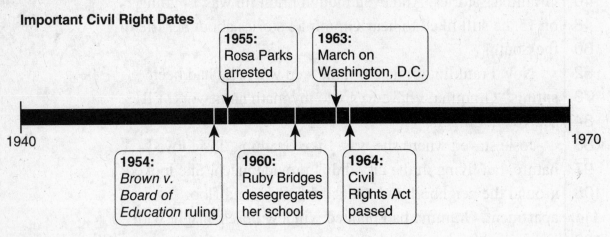

Important Civil Right Dates

1955:
Rosa Parks arrested

1963:
March on Washington, D.C.

1940

1970

1954:
Brown v. Board of Education ruling

1960:
Ruby Bridges desegregates her school

1964:
Civil Rights Act passed

1. What is this time line about? _____

_____

2. What happened in 1955? _____

3. What happened first: the Civil Rights Act or the *Brown v. Board*

of Education ruling? _____

4. To which city did civil rights protesters march in 1963? _____

5. Would Rosa Parks have been arrested for refusing to give up her seat after

1964? Explain your answer. _____

_____

6. Where would this event appear on the time line? In 1946, the United States
Supreme Court bans segregation on buses that travel across state lines.

_____

_____

At Home: Draw a time line of the events in the past year of
your life.

Name _____

> **Homophones** are words that sound the same but have different spellings and different meanings. Sometimes you need to read the words around a homophone to know which spelling and meaning makes the most sense.

A. Write the word from the box that best completes each sentence.

fair	their	way	bored
fare	there	weigh	board

Grandma always gives me bus _____ to go downtown. I

_____ the bus and sit in the last seat. It isn't _____

that I have to sit in the back, but I'm never _____. I watch people

carry _____ packages. Those bundles must _____

so much! I ride the bus all the _____ to the library. I'm so happy

when I'm _____.

B. Circle the two homophones in each sentence. Then answer the question.

1. The wind blew my blue hat away.

   Which word refers to a color? _____

2. I had to write the right word for each item on the test.

   Which word means correct? _____

3. Marta took one more turn and won the spelling bee.

   Which word means that someone has gained victory? _____

4. It is great to live in our state's capital because we can visit the capitol any time.

   Which word refers to a building? _____

At Home: Write five pairs of homophones on index cards. Write a sentence for each word.

Goin' Someplace Special
Grade 5/Unit 4

117

Many words have unaccented final syllables. Some of these words end with the **/əl/ sound,** as you hear in the word *bottle*. Other words have a final **/ən/ sound,** as you hear in the word *sharpen*. The final /əl/ may be spelled as **-el, -le, -il** or **-al.** The final /ən/ may be spelled as **-en, -in, -an, -on,** or **-ain.**

Circle the word in each pair that has a final unaccented syllable containing the /əl/ or /ən/ sound. Then write the letters that make the final sound in each word you circled.

1. human   moan   _____

2. winner   basin   _____

3. signal   prevail   _____

4. tell   angel   _____

5. nozzle   tale   _____

6. bacon   zone   _____

7. train   captain   _____

8. global   bale   _____

9. barrel   sell   _____

10. real   able   _____

11. listen   lessened   _____

12. practical   all   _____

13. slogan   lagoon   _____

14. will   pencil   _____

15. rain   mountain   _____

At Home: Find five more words with the /əl/ and /ən/ sound in an unaccented final syllable in a magazine article or book.

© Macmillan/McGraw-Hill

Name _____

A. In the sentences below circle correct if the boldface vocabulary word is used properly. If not, circle incorrect.

1. The boring television show was **arousing** the children's interest.

   correct   **incorrect**

2. The baby deer that was **nestled** in the grass looked peaceful.

   correct   **incorrect**

3. The **secluded** spot was ideal for a picnic because it was out in the open where everyone could see it.

   correct   **incorrect**

4. The boy knocked on the doors of all the **arroyo** in the village to apologize for the smell of his shoes.

   correct   **incorrect**

5. The **unpleasant** encounter with the skunk is one of Carlos's unhappiest memories.

   correct   **incorrect**

6. The **behavior** of the animal's fur helps it blend in with its surroundings.

   correct   **incorrect**

B. Write two sentences that use the vocabulary word correctly.

7. **stunned** _____

   _____

8. **glimpse** _____

   _____

Authors have a purpose, or reason, for writing. An **author's purpose** might be to persuade, to inform, or to entertain.

Read each passage below. On the lines provided, write whether the author's main purpose is to persuade, to inform, or to entertain. Then write a sentence to explain your answer.

1. If you're thinking of finding a new hobby, then you should seriously consider bird-watching. First of all, it involves spending time outdoors. Many trips are planned with groups of people, so bird-watching is a good way to make new friends. Best of all, you get to see many interesting birds. Pick up your binoculars today!

   Author's purpose: _____

   _____

   _____

2. I frantically called to my dog Frisky, but it was already too late. She had spotted the skunk and was running after it happily. Frisky just wanted to play, but the skunk didn't know that. As the skunk lifted its tail, Frisky leaned down to get a sniff, and the skunk sprayed her right in the face. Poor Frisky! And poor me! I had to give her a bath.

   Author's purpose: _____

   _____

   _____

3. A skunk is a small, furry animal with black and white markings. Skunks are part of the weasel family. They are best known for the highly offensive liquid that they spray when they are frightened. This smelly liquid is called musk. A skunk can spray its musk as far as ten feet.

   Author's purpose: _____

   _____

   _____

© Macmillan/McGraw-Hill

At Home: Read aloud a newspaper or magazine article to identify the author's purpose, and explain how you reached that conclusion.

Name _____

As you read *Carlos and the Skunk*, fill in the Author's Purpose Chart.

Clues	Author's Purpose

How does the information you wrote in the Author's Purpose Chart help you evaluate *Carlos and the Skunk*?

At Home: Have student use the chart to retell the story.

© Macmillan/McGraw-Hill

As I read, I will pay attention to intonation.

	Lizards, turtles, and snakes are all reptiles. They live in
10	a world full of danger. Predators are on the prowl, looking
21	to eat reptiles that aren't careful. Animals may try to steal
32	their territory or their eggs, or eat them. Reptiles aren't
42	helpless though. They have many defenses they can use to
52	protect themselves and their homes.
57	In the face of a threat, a reptile's usual behavior is to avoid
70	it. Lizards dart away. Snakes slither away. Turtles hide in
80	their shells or slip into the water. Escape is sometimes the
91	only way to live another day. Often, though, staying out of
102	trouble isn't possible. That's when a reptile uses its defenses
112	to help it stay alive. It may use color, size, special body parts,
125	or even deadly poison to survive. Read on to learn more.
136	Sometimes a reptile can't run away from danger. Most
145	will then try to scare the predator away. Some change the
156	way they stand. Others change the way they look. 165

Comprehension Check

1. What is the main idea of this passage? **Main Idea and Details**

2. What special defenses may reptiles use? **Main Idea and Details**

	Words Read	–	Number of Errors	=	Words Correct Score
First Read		–		=	
Second Read		–		=	

At Home: Help the student read the passage, paying attention to the goal at the top of the page.

Name _____

A **deck** is a short preview of a magazine article that is designed to grab the reader's attention. **Headings** are subtitles that break an article into different parts. They help readers organize information so it is easier to understand.

Read the magazine article "Animal Self-Defense." Then answer the questions.

> **Animal Self-Defense**
> by Elle Wainwright
>
> If you were a wild animal about to become someone's dinner, what would you do? Run? Hide? Fight? Animals may do any of these things when they feel threatened.
>
> **Hide and Seek**
> Some adaptations help animals hide. An animal can seem to disappear by using camouflage.

1. What is the title of the article? _____

2. What is the byline? _____
_____

3. What is the deck? _____
_____
_____
_____

4. What is the heading? _____
_____

At Home: Write a short magazine article about an animal that uses camouflage to protect itself. Label the title, byline, headings, and deck of your article.

You can define an unknown word by using **context clues,** the words around an unknown word that give you clues to the word's meaning.

Circle the context clues in each sentence that can help you figure out the meaning of the underlined word. Then write the definition of the underlined word on the line.

1. The skunk, <u>unaware</u> how badly Tina smelled after spraying her, walked away as if nothing happened.

   unaware: _____

2. The hiker was a <u>coward</u> and was frightened at even the smallest sound.

   coward: _____

3. The <u>location</u> of the town was unknown, but Tom believed he knew where the place was.

   location: _____

4. The boat had a tough time <u>navigating</u> the rough seas, but the dolphins had no problem making their way through the waves.

   navigating: _____

5. The thornbug's camouflage was <u>flawless</u>, and the students marveled at its perfect disguise.

   flawless: _____

6. He was so <u>grouchy</u> after being sprayed by the skunk that nothing could change his grumpy mood.

   grouchy: _____

7. The <u>pesky</u> mosquito annoyed the girl as it buzzed in her ear.

   pesky: _____

8. The cliffs marked the southern <u>boundary</u> of the village, and the river marked the northern edge.

   boundary: _____

At Home: Choose five of the underlined words above, and make up new context clues for them.

© Macmillan/McGraw-Hill

Accented syllables may have vowel sounds that are neither long nor short. Each of these vowel sounds can be spelled in several different ways.

Sound	Spelling	Example
/ou/	ou, ow	count, plow
/ô/	al, aw, au, ough	all, crawl, haul, thought
/oi/	oi, oy	boil, boy

Read the words below. Listen to the vowel sound in each accented syllable. Then place the words below in the correct column of the chart according to the vowel pattern in the accented syllable of each word.

flawless	thoughtless	loyal	foil
allow	power	grouchy	powder
applause	toiling	doubting	
toying	faucet	fall	

/ou/ (ou, ow)	/ô/ (al, aw, au, ough)	/oi/ (oi, oy)

At Home: Think of two additional words for each column of the chart.

compelled	presidential	disrespectful
unenthusiastically	succeed	preoccupied

A. Choose a word from the box that means the same as the italicized words or phrases. The write the word on the line.

Voting is an important right, but many people do not feel *the urge*

_____ to vote. It is especially important to vote

when the election is *for the president* _____. The

Vice President is also important because he or she can *follow in sequence*

_____ to the presidency, if something happens to

the president. Some people are *engrossed* _____

with their jobs and families and forget to vote. Many people respond *with no*

excitement _____ when given the chance to cast their

ballots. I even saw someone who was *rude* _____ to

workers at the polls because everyone had to wait a long time to vote. Yet, the

time and effort will pay off because voting on election day makes you feel

proud.

B. Write two sentences using a vocabulary word. Then underline the vocabulary word.

1. _____

    _____

2. _____

    _____

© Macmillan/McGraw-Hill

Name _____

> When you **make generalizations,** you make broad statements
> based on information from the text and your own knowledge.

Read the paragraph. Then answer the questions.

Typically, only a little more than half of voting-age Americans vote in a presidential election. There was only a 17% turnout of voters between the ages of 18 to 29 for the most recent presidential election. Volunteers send out e-mails, make phone calls, and go door-to-door to remind people to vote. Yet, there are many reasons people do not vote. Here are the top reasons people gave for not voting in a recent presidential election:

1. No time off or too busy	5. Out of town
2. Not interested	6. Other reasons
3. Ill, disabled, or had an emergency	7. Forgot
4. Did not like the candidates	

1. What generalization can you make about why most people do not vote?

   _____

2. Why do you think volunteers make phone calls, send e-mails, and go
   door-to-door asking people to vote? _____

   _____

3. What generalization can you make about voters who are 18 to 24 years old?

   _____

   _____

4. Why might someone make the generalization that it is disrespectful for
   people of voting age not to vote? _____

   _____

   _____

At Home: Write a generalization about why voting is an
important part of U.S. history.

Getting Out the Vote • **Grade 5/Unit 4** 127

© Macmillan/McGraw-Hill

As you read "Getting Out the Vote", fill in the Generalizations Chart.

Information from Text	
Prior Knowledge	
Generalizations	

How does the information you wrote in this Generalizations Chart help
you evaluate "Getting Out the Vote"?

At Home: Have the student use the chart to retell the story.

As I read, I will pay attention to pauses.

	Do you have strong feelings about something? Do others
9	feel differently? Often this can happen in families. Maybe
18	family members ask you to help keep your home clean.
28	They say that you live in the home, and it's **disrespectful**
39	for you to ignore your responsibility. On the other hand, the
50	mess does not bother you. You think that those who are
61	**preoccupied** with the mess should be the ones to clean it up.
73	Or your family members may point out that the ones who
84	pay the bills should make the rules of the house. You think
96	that everyone in the house should help make the rules.
106	A debate like this may go back and forth for some time.
118	Each person tries to convince the others that he or she
129	is right. In a situation like this one, no one is really right
142	or wrong. Yet each person wants to win. What is the
153	answer? 154

Comprehension Check

1. Who do some family members think should make the rules? **Main Idea and Details**

2. What is a debate? **Main Idea and Details**

	Words Read	–	Number of Errors	=	Words Correct Score
First Read		–		=	
Second Read		–		=	

© Macmillan/McGraw-Hill

At Home: Help the student read the passage, paying attention to the goal at the top of the page.

If you can identify the **parts of a book,** you can easily find the information that you need.

Read the chart below. Then write the correct part of a book to answer each question.

Front of a book	Back of a book
Title page: tells the book's title and author	**Index:** an alphabetical listing of names and topics and the page numbers that apply to each item
Chapter titles: tells the names of the chapters	**Glossary:** an alphabetical list of words and definitions
Table of contents: lists the chapter titles and the page number on which each chapter begins	**Endnotes:** notes that give additional information
	Bibliography: a list of writings that includes the date and place of publication

1. Which part of a book has notes that give additional information? _____

2. In which part of a book can you find the definitions of words? _____

3. Where can you find the first page number of a chapter? _____

4. Which two parts of a book are arranged in alphabetical order? _____

   _____

5. How could you learn whether a topic or person you are researching is

   mentioned in a book? _____

6. How could you find information about books or articles that an author used

   to write the book you are reading? _____

At Home: Identify each part of a favorite book. Write the names of the parts you find, including any that are not mentioned in the list above.

Name _____

> **Prefixes** and **suffixes** are word parts that can be added to a word
> to change the word's meaning. A prefix is added to the beginning
> of a word, and a suffix is added to the end of a word.

Prefixes	Meaning	Suffixes	Meanings
dis-	not	*-ial*	having to do with
un-	not	*-ful*	showing, full of
re-	anew, again	*-ly, -ally*	in the manner of

**Write the prefix, suffix, or both for each word. Write the word's meaning.
Then use the word in a sentence.**

1. restart   **Prefix:** _____   **Suffix:** _____

   Meaning: _____

   Sentence: _____

2. disrespectful   **Prefix:** _____   **Suffix:** _____

   Meaning: _____

   Sentence: _____

3. presidential   **Prefix:** _____   **Suffix:** _____

   Meaning: _____

   Sentence: _____

4. unenthusiastically   **Prefix:** _____   **Suffix:** _____

   Meaning: _____

   Sentence: _____

5. residential   **Prefix:** _____   **Suffix:** _____

   Meaning: _____

   Sentence: _____

At Home: Write five prefixes and five suffixes on slips of
paper. Then take turns adding each prefix or suffix to a
base word.

Homographs are words that are spelled the same way but have different meanings. Sometimes words that are homographs will be accented, or stressed, on different syllables. The part of speech and the meaning of the word depends on which syllable is accented.

Circle the syllable in each underlined homograph that should be accented to make the sentence correct. Use a dictionary to help you.

1. An election is a <u>contest</u> between two or more candidates.

2. The lawyer will <u>contest</u> the decision the judge made.

3. Candidates must watch their <u>conduct</u> while debating each other.

4. The maestro will <u>conduct</u> the orchestra.

5. The <u>conflict</u> was broadcast on television.

6. Luckily, her schedule did not <u>conflict</u> with ours.

7. Politics is a <u>subject</u> that many people feel strongly about.

8. The king did not <u>subject</u> his people to cruel punishments.

9. Every <u>minute</u> detail must be followed in the line of presidential succession.

10. A <u>minute</u> passed before I was called into the doctor's office.

11. He will probably <u>refuse</u> to run in the election.

12. Tim does not throw <u>refuse</u> in the recycling bin.

13. I am <u>content</u> to live in a democracy that offers so many freedoms.

14. The <u>content</u> of her speech was in the outline.

At Home: Look up five more homographs that have different syllables accented. Then write a sentence for each word.

Name _____

A. Select the correct word from the vocabulary words within the parentheses. Then write your choice on the line.

(Hurricanes / Atmospheres) _____ are tropical storms with

rain and strong swirling winds. Hurricanes form over the ocean where warm

water is (available / beautiful) _____ as a source of energy.

The (property / atmosphere) _____ surrounding a hurricane

uses moisture from the warm water to power the storm. When a hurricane

moves toward land, a (surge / destruction) _____ of water

can cause flooding in coastal areas. When a hurricane finally makes

(waves / contact) _____ with the land, high winds

are a serious threat. These powerful storms can cause much

(destruction / atmosphere) _____ to (surges / property)

_____. The cost of (contacts / damages) _____

from a hurricane can reach billions of dollars.

B. Write your own paragraph about hurricanes using at least three vocabulary words. Then underline each vocabulary word.

_____

_____

_____

_____

_____

_____

_____

_____

> **Description** is a way nonfiction text can be organized or
> structured. Signal words such as *first, next, then,* or *finally* will
> alert you to descriptive facts in a text.

Read the paragraph. Then answer the questions below.

Hurricane Andrew was one of the worst hurricanes to hit the United
States. Andrew first formed in the warm waters of the southern Atlantic
Ocean in August 1992. The storm had winds of only 40 miles per hour. As
the storm continued to move over the warm ocean, it gained energy and grew
stronger. When the wind speed reached 74 miles per hour, the storm was
officially a hurricane and was named Andrew. Then Andrew's winds climbed
to 155 miles per hour! Next heavy rain moved onshore as Andrew made
landfall in southern Florida. Seven inches of rain fell, and storm tides were as
high as 17 feet. Hurricane Andrew caused significant destruction to property
in the United States. Final damages eventually totaled $25 billion.

1. What was the first fact the author gives about the storm that became

   Hurricane Andrew? _____

   _____

2. What was the initial wind speed of the storm? _____

   _____

3. What signal word does the author use when describing Andrew's high

   wind speed? _____

4. The author uses *next* to alert you to what descriptive fact? _____

   _____

5. What were the final damage costs? _____

   _____

At Home: Write a brief story about a hurricane. Use signal
words to alert readers to descriptive facts.

As you read *Hurricanes*, fill in the Description Chart.

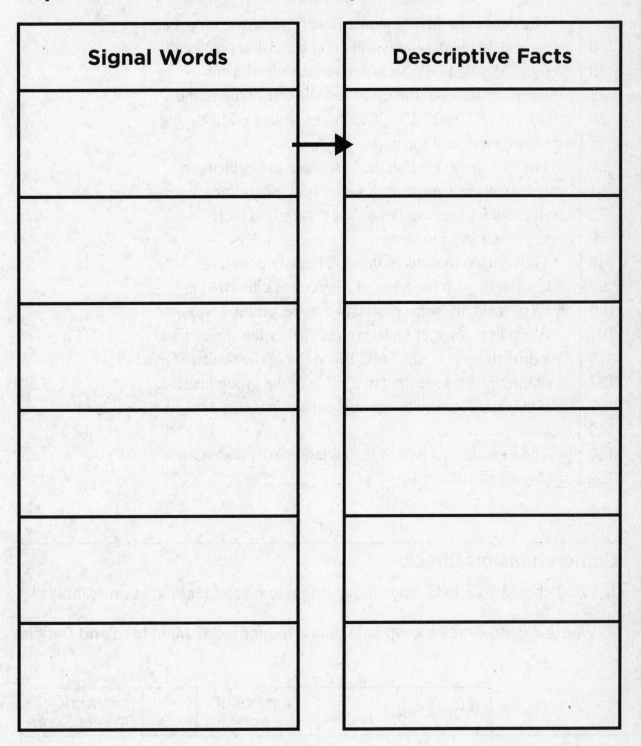

Signal Words	Descriptive Facts

How does the information you wrote in the Description Chart help you analyze the text structure of *Hurricanes*?

At Home: Have the student use the chart to retell the story.

Hurricanes • **Grade 5/Unit 4** 135

© Macmillan/McGraw-Hill

As I read, I will pay attention to pronunciation.

	The Brodie family—mother, father, two boys, three cats,
9	a dog, and an iguana—was watching television on Monday
19	evening, May 3, 1999. An afternoon thunderstorm was
25	creating tornadoes to the southwest of their home in the
35	suburbs of Oklahoma City, Oklahoma. It looked like a big
45	tornado was headed their way.
50	The Brodies knew that the best place to be during a
61	tornado is in the basement or under heavy furniture in a
72	small room without windows. They went into their
80	underground tornado shelter.
83	The tornado that swept through heavily populated
90	Oklahoma City on the night of May 3 was classified as
100	an F5 tornado, the most powerful ever recorded.
107	A group in another underground shelter felt the tornado
116	pass directly over their heads. The walls of the shelter started
127	to vibrate. Then, according to a witness, the group heard
137	"one big crack" as the house above them was lifted off its
149	foundation.
150	The tornado was part of the Oklahoma Tornado Outbreak
159	of May 1999. 161

Comprehension Check

1. What should you do to stay safe during a tornado? **Main Idea and Details**

2. Where did the Brodies keep safe during the tornado? **Main Idea and Details**

	Words Read	–	Number of Errors	=	Words Correct Score
First Read		–		=	
Second Read		–		=	

At Home: Help the student read the passage, paying attention to the goal at the top of the page.

Elements used in poetry include **personification,** or giving human characteristics to an animal, thing, or idea. Another element is **imagery,** or the use of descriptions to create vivid pictures in the reader's mind. Also **onomatopoeia,** or the use of words that imitate the sounds of an object or action is used in poetry.

Read the poems and answer the questions.

Rabbit Mother sings her babies to sleep.
Tells them not to worry about the rain that splashes down,
Or that flash of lighting and sudden crash of thunder.
Her babies safe in a hillside burrow and Rabbit Mother taps her toes.
Waiting out another hurricane.

1. What literary devices does the poem above contain? How do you know?

_____

_____

2. What examples of onomatopoeia are used to describe the hurricane?

_____

Hurricane
Spinning leaves, flowing water.
All rotating together.
Like water spinning down the drain of an enormous bathtub.
Clockwise in the South. Counterclockwise in the North.
No toys, no bubbles.
Only wind and rain, and the hope that soon all will be safely dried
With the fluffy towel of sunshine.

3. What literary device does this poem have? How do you know?

_____

_____

_____

🏠 **At Home:** Write a poem describing weather. Use at least
one example of personification, imagery, and onomatopoeia.

Practice

Name _____

Vocabulary Strategy:
Multiple-Meaning
Words

Words with more than one meaning are **multiple-meaning words.**
You can use context clues or other words in the sentence to
help you figure out the most appropriate meaning. Sometimes
you may need to consult a dictionary to find all the different
meanings of the word.

**Write a definition of the underlined word based on how it is used in
the sentence.**

1. When a hurricane's <u>eye</u> passes over you, the wind stops blowing.

   Eye means: _____

   _____.

2. An <u>eye</u> will allow you to see your surroundings.

   Eye means: _____

   _____.

3. Even during the worst of the storm, my mother maintained her <u>image</u>
   of calm.

   Image means: _____

   _____.

4. The postcard had an <u>image</u> of a very famous painting on it.

   Image means: _____

   _____.

5. A hurricane <u>watch</u> was issued, so we prepared to leave.

   Watch means: _____

   _____.

6. My <u>watch</u> stopped keeping time because the battery died.

   Watch means: _____

   _____.

© Macmillan/McGraw-Hill

At Home: Read a passage from a book, magazine, or
newspaper. Then make a list of the multiple-meaning words
that you find.

Name _____

The sounds you hear in the final syllable of the words *culture* and *measure* can be spelled in different ways, including **-ture, -cher,** and **-sure**. Listen to the final syllables in the words *measure* (**/zhər/ sound**) and *culture* (**/chər/ sound**).

A. Choose the word in each pair that has a final syllable that sounds like the final syllable in *measure*. Then write the word on the line.

measure

1. searcher / azure _____

2. pleasure / rancher _____

3. seizure / fracture _____

4. mixture / treasure _____

5. enclosure / gesture _____

6. leisure / fixture _____

B. Choose the word in each pair that has a final syllable that sounds like the final syllable in *culture*. Then write the word on the line.

culture

7. legislature / leisure _____

8. future / azure _____

9. butcher / pleasure _____

10. seizure / nature _____

11. mixture / erasure _____

12. teacher / ledger _____

13. creature / enclosure _____

14. pressure / gesture _____

15. exposure / nurture _____

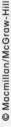

At Home: Write six sentences using three /chər/ words and three /zhər/ words. Read the sentences aloud to hear the sounds in the final syllables.

| appreciation | wares | treasurer | merchandise |
| educate | burdens | riverbank | unfortunate |

Replace the underlined word or words in each sentence with a word from the box.

1. The story of the fisher can <u>teach</u> readers about how people's greed can often get them in trouble. _____

2. The fisher sat by the <u>edge of the river</u> and thought of a way to trick people. _____

3. The Market Club hired a <u>person who manages money</u> to help count all the money made at the market. _____

4. At the market, the basket-maker set out her <u>collection of wares</u> for all to see. _____

5. The fisher tricked others into leaving part of their <u>heavy loads</u> with him. _____

6. Each person carefully carried his or her <u>products</u> across the log in order to reach the market. _____

7. He hoped that people would express their <u>gratitude</u> by paying him well. _____

8. The fisher's plan did not work, and he felt very <u>unlucky</u>. _____

An **author's purpose** is his or her reason for writing the story. The purpose may be to inform, to entertain, to persuade, or to instruct.

Read the summary of *The Catch of the Day*. Then answer the questions about the author's purpose.

   A Griot introduced himself as a keeper of history, a teacher, and a storyteller, and told a group of children a story of a fisher who decided to trick many people who were trying to get to the market. The fisher shook a log to convince each person it was unsafe to cross with so much merchandise. Finally, the ones who were tricked discovered what the Fisher was up to and decided to trick him. As the fisher crossed the bridge they shook the log so hard that he fell into the water. On the riverbank, the people the fisher tricked laughed and laughed. And later that day they ate a fine fish dinner!

1. When the Griot explains who he is, is the author's main purpose to inform, to entertain, to persuade, or to instruct? Explain.

   _____

   _____

2. When the author describes how the Fisher was tricked, is her main purpose to entertain, to inform, to persuade, or to instruct? Explain.

   _____

   _____

3. In what ways might the author's purpose be to persuade people?

   _____

   _____

4. What do you think is the author's purpose for writing *The Catch of the Day*?

   _____

   _____

© Macmillan/McGraw-Hill

At Home: Find a story that was written to entertain, to persuade, to inform, or to instruct. Write a paragraph about how you can tell that this is the purpose.

The Catch of the Day
Grade 5/Unit 4

141

Name _____

As you read *The Catch of the Day*, fill in the Author's Purpose Chart.

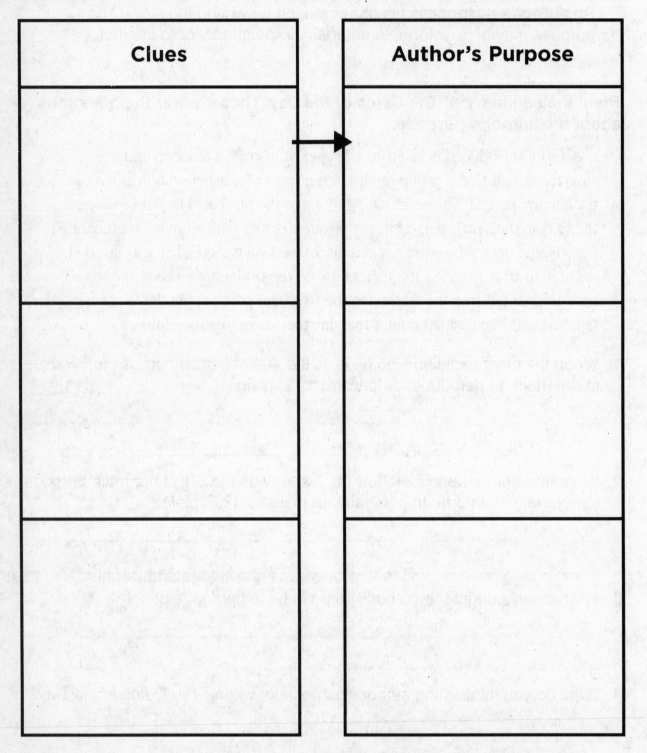

Clues	Author's Purpose

How does the information you wrote in the Author's Purpose Chart help
you evaluate *The Catch of the Day*?

At Home: Have the student use the chart to retell the story.

© Macmillan/McGraw-Hill

Name _____

As I read, I will pay attention to tempo.

	NARRATOR 1: Well, at least it isn't a raging river that Brer
11	Rabbit has to cross, just a creek. Though it is higher than
23	usual, and the rain is still coming down hard.
32	**BRER RABBIT:** *(to the audience)* Well, that wasn't too bad.
42	If getting my feet a little wet is the most **unfortunate** thing
54	that happens tonight, I'll be just fine. *(He shakes off the*
65	*wetness and looks around. Then, putting his hand to his ear,*
76	*he listens for a moment.)* Music! I do believe I hear a party
89	shaping up! *(He rubs his hands together eagerly.)* And that
99	means dancing, and dancing means food to feed the dancers,
109	and that means a fine time is had by all. *(He heads offstage*
122	*with a hop, skip, and a jump.)*
129	**NARRATOR 2:** And indeed, a fine time is had by all,
139	especially Brer Rabbit, who doesn't give another thought to
148	the weather. He tries every dance and every dish and finds
159	them all to his total satisfaction. 165

Comprehension Check

1. What does Brer Rabbit enjoy about parties? **Main Idea and Details**

2. How does Brer Rabbit feel about the weather? **Make Inferences**

	Words Read	–	Number of Errors	=	Words Correct Score
First Read		–		=	
Second Read		–		=	

At Home: Help the student read the passage, paying attention to the goal at the top of the page.

The Catch of the Day
Grade 5/Unit 4

143

© Macmillan/McGraw-Hill

A fable is a short story that teaches a lesson, or **moral**. One particular kind of fable is the trickster fable. **Metaphor** is a type of figurative language that compares things or actions without using *like* or *as*.

Read the fable. Then answer the questions.

A crow kept an eye on a family having a picnic. While she waited for them to finish she took a dip in a pond and spent a long time looking at her reflection in the water. When her stomach grumbled, she returned to the picnic site. The family had left but left a piece of cheese behind. She clamped the cheese in her beak and flew to a branch. Then a fox appeared and smelled the cheese. He soon spotted the crow. The fox flattered the crow: "Your feathers must be of the finest onyx." Next, the fox asked to hear her sweet voice that surely must match her magnificent feathers. The crow opened her beak to sing and dropped the cheese. The fox scooped up the cheese and ate it. He told her to think before she acts.

1. Write the moral of this fable.

   _____

   _____

2. Why does the trickster decide to trick the other character?

   _____

   _____

3. Give an example of the use of metaphor.

   _____

   _____

4. Describe the trick.

   _____

   _____

   _____

 At Home: Write a trickster fable. Make sure you include a metaphor and a moral.

© Macmillan/McGraw-Hill

An analogy shows the **relationship** between two pairs of words. The relationship between the two words in the first pair is the same as the relationship between the two words in the second pair.

drink	story	crops	baskets	fingers
fox	merchandise	hopping	leather	fish
song	eagle	painter	needle	mailbox

Choose a word from the box to complete each analogy.

1. Banker is to money as farmer is to _____.

2. Library is to books as store is to _____.

3. Bird is to flying as rabbit is to _____.

4. Baker is to bread as basketmaker is to _____.

5. Nibble is to eat as sip is to _____.

6. Yam is to vegetable as trout is to _____.

7. Clap is to hands as snap is to _____.

8. Vain is to crow as sneaky is to _____.

9. Shirt is to cloth as shoes are to _____.

10. Poet is to poem as author is to _____.

11. Griot is to story as singer is to _____.

12. Dog is to wolf as parrot is to _____.

13. Microscope is to scientist as paintbrush is to _____.

14. Email is to computers as letter is to _____.

At Home: Write four analogies that show the relationship between two pairs of words.

The suffixes **-ance** and **-ence** mean "the state or quality of." They are suffixes with unstressed vowels.

Complete each word by adding -ance or -ence. Then write the completed word on the line. Use a dictionary to help you find the syllable that is stressed. Say each new word to hear how it is pronounced. Circle the stressed syllable in each word.

1. ambul_____ _____

2. resid_____ _____

3. bal_____ _____

4. subst_____ _____

5. import_____ _____

6. assist_____ _____

7. abs_____ _____

8. persist_____ _____

9. attend_____ _____

10. disturb_____ _____

11. independ_____ _____

12. perform_____ _____

13. refer_____ _____

14. eleg_____ _____

15. emerg_____ _____

 At Home: Use five words in a sentence. Read the five sentences aloud stressing the correct syllable of the *-ance* or *-ence* word.

© Macmillan/McGraw-Hill

Name _____

A. From each pair of words in parentheses, choose the word that best completes each sentence, and write it on the line.

1. The laser lightshow was a (secluded/spectacular) _____ display of color and light.

2. The (surge/permission) _____ of the tides often reached the highest points of the beach.

3. The students showed their (behavior/appreciation) _____ by giving the principal a plaque when she retired.

4. The increasingly cold weather (blurted/compelled) _____ us to put on our warmest coats.

5. The sculptor (chiseled/clenched) _____ his name in the statue.

6. I asked the celebrity for his (autograph/contact) _____ to prove to my friends that I met him.

B. Use the words from the box to fill in the blanks in the paragraph below.

> damages   hurricanes   riverbank   available   destruction   wares

   After the _____ struck, everything changed.

The fierce storms caused a great deal of _____, and

_____ were high. The market along the _____

was hit especially hard. The river flooded its banks, and many merchants

lost their _____. Although it was difficult to recover from the

storms, the townspeople found support from neighbors who made food and

supplies _____.

**A. Match each word on the left with its synonym on the right.
Write the letter of your choice on the line provided.**

1. ____ available   **a.** teach

2. ____ stunned   **b.** dazed

3. ____ preoccupied   **c.** follow

4. ____ succeed   **d.** payment

5. ____ educate   **e.** unoccupied

6. ____ fare   **f.** distracted

**B. Choose the adjective from the box that best describes each
noun phrase. Use each adjective only once. Then use the
adjective in a sentence.**

presidential unpleasant clenched nestled secluded unfortunate

7. A hidden or hard-to-find area _____

   _____

8. an election for the leadership of the United States _____

   _____

9. a run of bad luck _____

   _____

10. the way an animal has curled up snugly in the grass _____

    _____

11. a sensation that causes discomfort _____

    _____

12. a tightly closed fist _____

    _____

Name _____

| abandon | treacherous | expedition | uninhabited |
| dismantled | labor | triumph | frigid |

A. Write the vocabulary word that best completes each sentence.

1. Glaciers can be _____ because they have deep holes hidden under thin ice.

2. The scientist wanted to go on an _____ to the North Pole to learn more about the animals that live there.

3. Scientists _____ in the freezing weather to build a station.

4. The _____ water was hard for the boat to navigate through because of all the ice and snow.

5. People have been known to _____ over the tough environment at the North Pole.

6. They _____ the tents and packed the pieces onto the boat.

7. The early explorers had to _____ their shacks when they left Antarctica.

8. Until recently, Antarctica was _____ by humans.

B. Read each question. Then write the vocabulary word that best answers the question.

9. If you were on a special mission with a specific purpose, what would you be on? _____

10. What is another word for "be successful" or "win"? _____

11. If a building was not lived in for a very long time, what would it be?

    _____

12. How would you describe a road with dangerous curves and no sidewalks?

    _____

Name _____

Read each of the following passages from *Spirit of Endurance*. For each passage, tell what problem Shackleton and his crew faced. Explain how they solved the problem.

The crew dismantled the dogloos and brought all the animals back on board because they were afraid that the ice would break under the dogs.

Problem: _____

_____

Solution: _____

_____

Luckily, the destruction of *Endurance* happened in slow motion. This gave the crew plenty of time to unload food and equipment. As the ship continued to break up, the pile of gear on the ice grew larger. Everything that could be taken off the ship was removed. The crew worked without a break. Their survival would depend on saving everything that might come in handy.

Problem: _____

_____

Solution: _____

_____

Their mountaineering equipment wasn't the best gear they could have wished for on a climb such as this one. They had an ax and fifty feet of rope. They studded the soles of their boots with nails for a better grip on the icy peaks. They rested for several days. Then, with food for three days and a small camping stove, they set out, crossing the first snowfield by moonlight.

Problem: _____

_____

Solution: _____

_____

© Macmillan/McGraw-Hill

At Home: Write a paragraph describing a problem you have solved.

Name _____

As you read *Spirit of Endurance*, fill in the Problem and Solution Map.

Problem

Attempt		Outcome
	➤	

Attempt		Outcome
	➤	

Attempt		Outcome
	➤	

Solution

How does the information you wrote in the Problem and Solution Map
help you generate questions about *Spirit of Endurance*?

At Home: Have the student use the chart to retell the story.

As I read, I will pay attention to pronunciation.

	Imagine planning an expedition to Mars today. What
8	would you wear? What would you eat? How would you travel
19	on Mars's surface? In 1900 the North and South Poles were
29	almost as alien to explorers as Mars is to us today. Because
41	the Poles are the farthest points from the sun all year long,
53	they don't receive its warmth and strong light. Each has an
64	extremely cold, dry climate. They are places of ice and snow.
75	The North and South Poles are similar. But they have
85	differences, too. The North Pole is surrounded by water. In
95	winter it is frozen solid, but in summer the ice breaks up. The
108	South Pole is land. It's a continent called Antarctica that has
119	mountains, valleys, and plains. When it is summer on the
129	North Pole, it is winter at the South Pole. They are as far
142	from each other as it is possible to be on Earth.
153	Both places have little food or shelter. There are no trees.
164	It is bitterly cold. 168

Comprehension Check

1. How are the North and South Poles alike and different? **Compare and Contrast**

2. Why are the Poles the coldest places on Earth? **Main Idea and Details**

	Words Read	–	Number of Errors	=	Words Correct Score
First Read		–		=	
Second Read		–		=	

© Macmillan/McGraw-Hill

At Home: Help the student read the passage, paying attention to the goal at the top of the page.

> A primary source is information that comes from the time being studied. **Journals** and **letters** are two types of primary sources. Journals provide daily records written by a person for his or her own use. Letters are a way for people to share information with others through writing.

Use the passage to answer the questions.

October 12

    The group and I arrived safely in Antarctica today. The wildlife here is wonderful! I already have seen a colony of Adelie penguins and managed to make some sketches of them in my notebook.

    The Adelie penguin

—has a white front and a black back.

—has a white ring around its eyes.

—is about 30 inches tall.

—weighs 11 pounds.

—eats fish. (Must remember to learn more about their diet tomorrow.)

1. What type of primary source is the passage above? How can you tell?

    _____

    _____

    _____

2. In what ways does the primary source show that the author has witnessed the events described?

    _____

    _____

    _____

3. Based on the passage, what is another primary source that you can expect to see with this one?

    _____

© Macmillan/McGraw-Hill

At Home: Keep a journal for a week. Then write a letter to a family member summarizing the daily events in your journal.

Name _____

> A **base word** is a word that can stand alone. A **root word** is a word part that forms the core of a longer word. Base and root words can be changed by adding **affixes**. Affixes are word parts such as prefixes that are added to the beginnings of a word or suffixes that are added to the end of a word. For example, the prefix *un-* means "not." The suffix *-able* means "able to." When these affixes are added to the root word *bear*, they form the new word *unbearable*, meaning "not able to bear."

For each word, find the root or base word. Then rewrite the word, dividing it into its parts by drawing slashes. Underline the root or base word.

1. unbreakable _____

2. unkindness _____

3. independence _____

4. leadership _____

5. abandonment _____

6. international _____

7. worthless _____

8. autograph _____

9. preview _____

10. transportable _____

© Macmillan/McGraw-Hill

At Home: Write a list of words that have the root word *sign*. Write another list of words that have the base word *new*. Add affixes to each word on your lists.

Name _____

Some words that are spelled with the letter *g* have a hard *g* sound.

Bag, *rug*, *gone*, and *igloo* are examples of words with the hard *g* sound.

Some other words have a **soft g** sound. *Age*, *edge*, *engine*, *gentle*, and *giraffe* are examples of words with a soft *g* sound. The *g* is usually soft when followed by *e*, *i*, or *y*. Some words with the **soft g** sound are spelled with *j* instead of with *g*.

Say aloud the words below. Circle each word that has a soft g sound.

1. major

2. village

3. guess

4. barge

5. agile

6. eggshell

7. grind

8. urgent

9. dodge

10. jolt

11. journal

12. margin

13. village

14. inject

15. surge

16. goggles

17. glaciers

18. enlarge

19. legend

20. range

At Home: Look in a book or a magazine to help you find ten more words that have the soft *g* sound.

| bedlam | civilization | shortage | outcast |
| traditional | strategy | complex | reflected |

A. Choose words from the box to complete the sentences below.

1. When fall came, there was no _____ of fruit from the large orchard.

2. The shiny leaves _____ the bright light of the afternoon sun.

3. The gymnasium was _____ after the basketball team won the championship.

4. Breeding hybrid fruits and vegetables is _____ work, but eating them is simple.

5. The teacher taught his students to always include everyone and not to make anyone feel like an _____.

6. Dusting the plants with flour was part of their _____ to protect the tomato plants from insects.

7. Our _____ holiday dessert is apple pie.

8. Our _____ has a long history of growing grain to feed people and trading the extra grain for other goods.

B. Possible definitions of the vocabulary words are below. Circle whether the given definition is true or false.

9. T F   strategy: a careful plan

10. T F   outcast: a well-liked individual

11. T F   shortage: an abundance or a large amount

12. T F   complex: hard to understand or do

The **theme** of a story is the overall message that the author expresses to readers. To identify the theme, think about what the characters in a story do.

Read the passage. Then answer the questions.

Wesley often found new ways of doing things that he liked better than the ordinary ways.

Some of Wesley's ideas helped him prove himself to the other children in the neighborhood. Before Wesley founded Weslandia, the children in the neighborhood had teased him because they did not understand him. Instead of fitting in by imitating the others, Wesley made friends by being himself.

1. Why did the other children tease Wesley? _____

_____

_____

2. Do you think the author believes that imitating other people to get along is a good idea? Explain your answer.

_____

_____

_____

3. Do you agree with the author's opinion? Explain your answer.

_____

_____

_____

4. What is the theme or message of the story? Explain.

_____

_____

_____

© Macmillan/McGraw-Hill

At Home: Read a book or passage and identify the theme.
Write a paragraph about the author's overall message.

As you read *Weslandia*, fill in the Theme Chart.

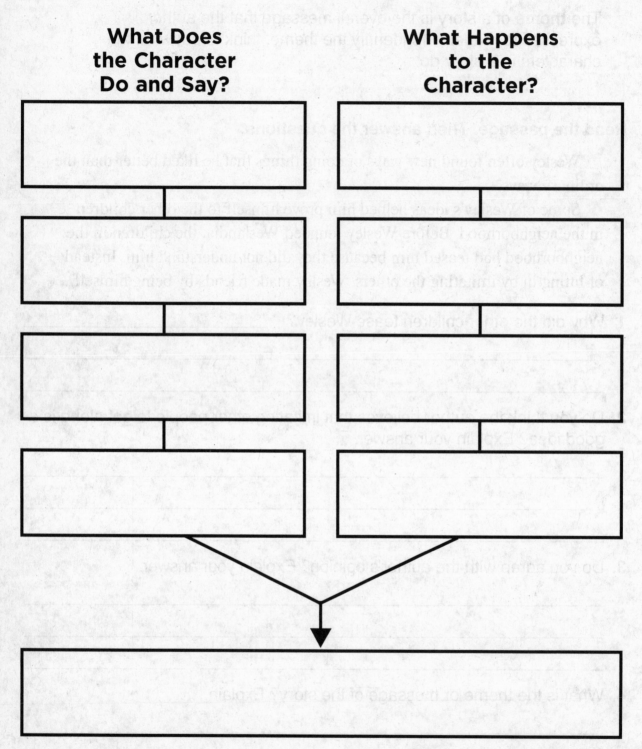

**What Does
the Character
Do and Say?**

**What Happens
to the
Character?**

How does the information you wrote in the Theme Chart help you make
inferences and analyze *Weslandia*?

At Home: Have the student use the chart to retell the story.

© Macmillan/McGraw-Hill

As I read, I will pay attention to punctuation.

	I handed in my Jupiter report today, but I don't remember
11	anything about the planet. That's because as soon as I got
22	home, excitement ruled. I could hear the noise about half a
33	mile away. When I got to the farm, there was **bedlam**!
44	"Well, if you didn't plant it, then how did it get here?"
56	I heard my mother yelling. My father said he didn't know how
68	the peculiar plant got there but that it had to be gotten rid of
82	right away. He didn't want our crop to be spoiled by some
94	mystery fruit.
96	"Hey, what's going on?" I asked over all the commotion.
106	"This!" shouted my mother as she pointed to a strange tree
117	in the middle of the orchard.
123	At first glance, when I looked at the tree, it looked like all
136	the other trees. But then I noticed the extraordinary fruit. Each
147	piece was round and yellow and had a big red spot on it. There
161	was just one spot and each piece of fruit was the same. 173

Comprehension Check

1. What is the problem? **Problem and Solution**

2. Why does the father plan to get rid of the tree? **Main Idea and Details**

	Words Read	–	Number of Errors	=	Words Correct Score
First Read		–		=	
Second Read		–		=	

At Home: Help the student read the passage, paying attention to the goal at the top of the page.

A **hyperlink** is an electronic connection within text on a Web page that provides direct access to other documents or information.
A **key word** is a specific word that helps you find information.

Look at the sample online encyclopedia entry. Then answer the questions.

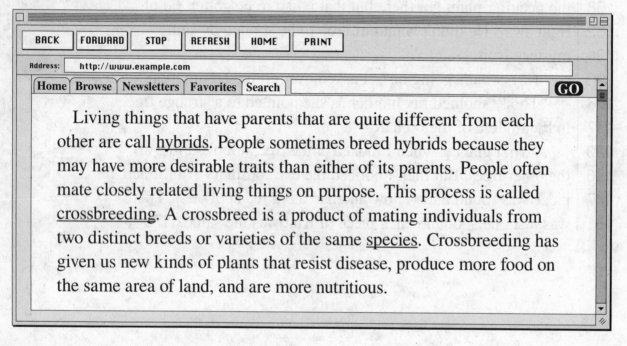

1. What are the hyperlinks on this page?

   _____

2. If you wanted to find out about different cat breeds, where would you type this information? What key words would you use?

   _____

3. If you wanted more information about different species, which hyperlink could you click on? How would you know?

   _____

   _____

At Home: Use hyperlinks and keywords to research information about a specific hybrid. Write a paragraph about what you learned.

© Macmillan/McGraw-Hill

Name _____

Use a dictionary when you want to check **word origins**. The definition may include information about the word's beginnings or how it has changed over time. It also may tell which language a word comes from or how or when a word became part of the English language.

Find each of these words in the dictionary. Next to each word, tell from which language the word comes.

1. taco _____

2. junk _____

3. car _____

4. reason _____

5. magenta _____

6. tortilla _____

7. city _____

8. dollar _____

9. guitar _____

10. cereal _____

11. music _____

12. radius _____

At Home: Find the people behind the origins of these words: *sandwich* and *teddy bear*.

> **Homophones** are words that sound alike but that have different spellings and different meanings. For example, the words *flour* and *flower* sound alike, but *flour* is used to make bread, and a *flower* is the bloom of a plant.

A. Choose the word that best completes each sentence. Circle the correct word.

1. They took a (poll/pole) to see which brand of cereal people liked best.

2. She did not like to (waist/waste) time watching television.

3. Dad ate toast with red (current/currant) jelly for breakfast.

4. My aunt is running for city (counsel/council).

5. We waited at the (peer/pier) for the boat to arrive.

6. Her (presence/presents) was very important at the meeting.

7. Who is going to (peal/peel) all of these potatoes?

8. The hotel (sweet/suite) was too expensive.

B. Write a sentence for each homophone.

9. accept: _____

_____

10. except: _____

_____

11. affect: _____

_____

12. effect: _____

_____

© Macmillan/McGraw-Hill

At Home: Make a list of six pairs of words that are homophones. Use each pair of homophones in a paragraph.

Choose the correct word that best completes the following sentences. Then write a new sentence with the word.

1. Our teacher tries to (instill/insert) a love of reading in each of us.

   _____

   _____

   _____

2. A (botanist/naturalist) is a person who studies nature. _____

   _____

   _____

3. The (singular/diverse) life in the park included many types of trees and wildlife.

   _____

   _____

   _____

4. We planted a neighborhood garden in the (busy/vacant) lot.

   _____

   _____

   _____

5. We (separated/combined) the soil with sand to help it drain well.

   _____

   _____

   _____

A **cause** is the reason why something happens, and an **effect** is the result, or the thing that happens.

Match the causes with their effects from the box. Write the letter of the effect on the line next to the cause.

Effects:

a. Lewis and Clark were sent to explore the new territory.

b. received help from friendly Native American tribes.

c. created accurate journals that described people, places, and things.

d. Lewis, Clark, and their team had very little to eat.

e. doubling the size of the United States

f. halting the expedition in order to catch one.

Causes:

1. Lewis and Clark took many breaks to write down everything they saw, which _____.

2. President Jefferson bought the Louisiana territory from France, thus _____.

3. The buffalo moved south for the winter, so _____.

4. Lewis and Clark did not know the land of the Louisiana Purchase, so they _____.

5. Lewis and Clark wanted to examine a prairie dog, which resulted in their _____.

6. President Jefferson wanted to find a water route to the Pacific Ocean, so _____.

© Macmillan/McGraw-Hill

At Home: Write a paragraph about the effects of Lewis and Clark's expedition of the Louisiana Purchase.

Name _____

As you read "A Historic Journey", fill in the Cause and Effect Chart.

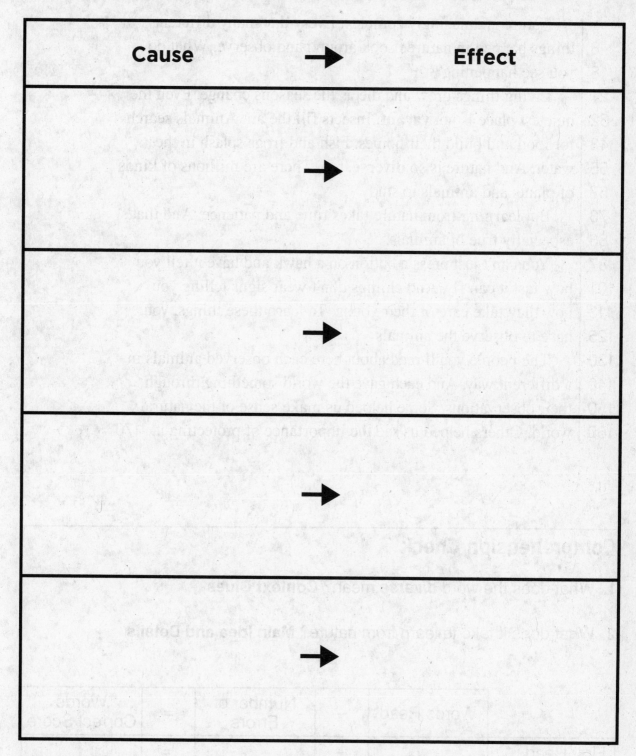

Cause	→	Effect
	→	
	→	
	→	
	→	

How does the information you wrote in this Cause and Effect Chart help you make inferences and analyze "A Historic Journey"?

At Home: Have the student use the chart to retell the story.

A Historic Journey • Grade 5/Unit 5   165

© Macmillan/McGraw-Hill

As I read, I will pay attention to punctuation.

	Nature is amazingly complex. Every day many different
8	things happen in nature. Look around and observe. What do
18	you see happening?
21	Living things grow and die as the seasons change. Even the
32	quietest place is not **vacant**. Insects fill the air. Animals search
43	for food and build their homes. Fish and frogs splash in the
55	water. And nature is so **diverse**, too. There are millions of kinds
67	of plants and animals to study.
73	But learning from nature takes time and patience. And that's
83	especially true of animals.
87	You can't just press a button on a hawk and have it tell you
101	how fast it can fly. And chimps don't wear signs telling you
113	how they take care of their young. To learn these things, you
125	have to observe the animals.
130	The people you'll read about here each observed animals in
140	a different way. And each gave the world something through
150	their observations. Some helped us make sense of the natural
160	world. Others helped us see the importance of protecting it. 170

Comprehension Check

1. What does the word *diverse* mean? **Context Clues**

2. What does it take to learn from nature? **Main Idea and Details**

	Words Read	–	Number of Errors	=	Words Correct Score
First Read		–		=	
Second Read		–		=	

© Macmillan/McGraw-Hill

At Home: Help the student read the passage, paying attention to the goal at the top of the page.

A **dictionary** entry tells you what a word means and how to pronounce it. It also tells whether a word is a noun, verb, or another part of speech. A **thesaurus** entry provides a list of words with similar meanings. It also contains parts of speech for each of the words.

Use the sample dictionary and thesaurus entries below to answer the questions.

Dictionary:
na-ture (´nā chər) *n.*: 1. the basic character of a person 2. the physical world, especially living things and objects such as rocks and air

Thesaurus:
Natural: n: normal, typical, regular
Natural: n: inherent, ingrained
Nature: n: type, kind

1. How many entries does the dictionary have for the word *nature*? _____

2. *Ingrained* is another word for _____.

3. Which definition of the word *nature* is the one studied by naturalists? How

   do you know? _____

   _____

4. Write the definition of *nature* that is used in this sentence: *True to her kind*

   nature, the social worker delivered meals to the elderly. _____

   _____

5. What are some other possible thesaurus entries for *nature*?

   _____

At Home: Find five words in the dictionary that have more than one definition. Write the different definitions in your own words. Then write five thesaurus entries.

Antonyms are words with opposite meanings A thesaurus
or dictionary is a tool that can help you find antonyms for a
particular word.

**A. Read the paragraph. Write the antonym from the box for each
underlined word.**

diverse	careful	incorrect	land	large	revealed

Lewis and Clark made a <u>small</u> _____ contribution
to exploration. Without them the secrets of the enormous <u>ocean</u>
_____ area known as the Louisiana Purchase may have
never been <u>hidden</u> _____. Lewis and Clark were the first
ones to explore the <u>same</u> _____ regions that make up the
United States. They passed through the Great Plains, Badlands, and Rocky
Mountains. They were very <u>careless</u> _____ about taking
<u>incorrect</u> _____ notes about the people, plants, and animals
they came across. With help from friendly Native American tribes, Lewis and
Clark made it all the way to the Pacific Ocean.

**B. Use the antonym word pairs from above to write four sentences.
Underline each antonym.**

1. _____

2. _____

3. _____

4. _____

At Home: Make a list of antonyms for the words *empty*,
different, and *huge*.

© Macmillan/McGraw-Hill

Name _____

> A ***prefix*** is an affix added to the front of a base or root word. By adding a prefix, you change the meaning of the word.
> *In-* means "without; not."
> *Dis-* means "opposite or lack of; not."
> *Mis-* means "bad or wrong."
> *Pre-* means "before."

Add *in-*, *dis-*, *mis-*, or *pre-* to each of the words in the sentences below. Use context clues to help you decide which prefix to use.

1. My teacher _____ approves of talking in class because it disturbs the other students.

2. A lumpy mattress can cause _____ comfort for your back.

3. You may need to _____ wash new clothes before you wear them.

4. The outfielder _____ judged the fly ball and did not make the catch.

5. You should not _____ judge food before you try it because you might actually like it.

6. My father _____ heats the oven before he puts the food in.

7. Rivals often _____ trust each other because they think the other person is trying to trick them.

8. The cheap toys were _____ expensive, so Mom agreed to buy them.

9. I _____ understood my teacher and wrote the wrong spelling word.

10. It is _____ honest to cheat on a test.

At Home: Write a sentence using the word *misjudge*. Write a second sentence using the word *prejudge*. Explain the difference.

A Historic Journey • Grade 5/Unit 5

enlisted	location	shield	reservation
invasion	corridor	sagged	creased

A. Choose a vocabulary word from the box to complete each sentence.

1. Grandfather said that his belief was his _____ from danger and kept him safe during the war.

2. The _____ of the class for the code talkers was secret.

3. His shoulders _____ at the thought of moving away from home.

4. We spoke both Navajo and English when we lived on the

   _____.

5. The _____ that led to the code talkers' classroom was long and narrow.

6. My grandfather's face was _____ from years of smiling and laughing.

7. Grandfather explained why he had _____ in the army when he was a young man.

8. The soldiers planned an _____ of enemy land.

B. Write two sentences, each using a vocabulary word.

9. _____

   _____

10. _____

    _____

The **author's perspective,** or point of view, is his or her opinion about the topic. The perspective affects how a story is written because the author chooses words and a tone that show his or her opinions, feelings, and beliefs.

Read each passage. Then answer the questions.

John raced up the trail, sending pebbles skidding behind him. When he reached his favorite hiding place, he fell to the ground out of breath. The river, full of late-summer rain, looked like a silver thread winding through his grandfather's farmland. They would be looking for him, but he was never coming down.

1. Explain the author's perspective on John's feelings.

_____

_____

2. What is the author's opinion about nature? How do you know?

_____

_____

His grandfather lifted him gently onto the horse. "The answer to that is in the code," he said. "The code name for America was 'Our Mother.' You fight for what you love. You fight for what is yours."

3. Explain how the author feels about the grandfather.

_____

_____

_____

4. What do you think the author's opinion is on protecting the United States?

_____

_____

© Macmillan/McGraw-Hill

At Home: Read a short story or a magazine article. Write a short paragraph that describes the author's perspective.

Name _____

As you read *The Unbreakable Code*, fill in the Author's Perspective Chart.

Clues	Author's Perspective

How does the information you wrote in the Author's Perspective Chart
help you generate questions about *The Unbreakable Code*?

At Home: Have the student use the chart to retell the story.

Name _____

As I read, I will pay attention to pauses and intonation.

	During the American Revolution, a woman named Anna
8	Smith Strong spied for the American patriots. She wanted to
18	help defeat the British, but she had to be very careful. If she
31	were caught, she would be sent to prison, or maybe even executed.
43	Anna Smith Strong thought of a simple way to pass
53	messages to the American patriots. She used her clothesline!
62	Everyone had to hang out laundry to dry in the 1700s. Who
73	would suspect that on her clothesline hung secret messages?
82	There were six coves near where Strong lived. The Americans
92	needed to know where a British ship was hiding. Strong used
103	her laundry to signal in which cove the ship was hiding. She
115	hung her black petticoat at one end of the line. Then she hung
128	up the correct number of creased, white handkerchiefs to identify
138	the proper cove. Strong helped pass on important information—
147	and she was never caught. 152

Comprehension Check

1. How did Anna Smith Strong send secret messages to American patriots? **Main Idea and Details**

2. What would hang on Anna Smith Strong's clothesline if a British ship was hiding in the fourth cove? **Draw Conclusions**

	Words Read	–	Number of Errors	=	Words Correct Score
First Read		–		=	
Second Read		–		=	

 At Home: Help the student read the passage, paying attention to the goal at the top of the page.

In poetry, **consonance** is the repetition of end consonant sounds in a series of words. **Symbolism** is the use of a concrete object to represent an abstract idea.

Read each cinquain below and then answer the questions.

Brother	1
Tell us about	2
Fellow brave and fearless	3
Navajo saved country and lives	4
And hope.	5

1. Which word shows consonance with fearless in line 3? _____

2. How could line 5 be rewritten to continue the consonance in line 4?

_____

Warning	1
Coding of words	2
In the puzzle of war	3
"Iron Fish" waiting underwater	4
Lives saved.	5

3. Which words in lines 3 and 4 show consonance? _____

4. The words "Iron Fish" probably symbolize which wartime vehicle?

_____

5. Why might using a symbol in a poem interest the reader more than simply

stating what the symbol represents? _____

_____

_____

At Home: List five or more interesting places and things in your neighborhood. Write 3 cinquains about those places or things that include consonance and symbolism.

Name _____

You can often figure out what an unfamiliar word is by using **context clues,** which are found by looking at other words in the sentence or in surrounding sentences.

Circle all the context clues that help you define the underlined word in each sentence.

1. During the drills, we said the same code over and over. We hoped that by <u>repeating</u> the code many times, it would be easy to remember.

2. Henry heard the wind always. The noise of the wind in the canyons especially was <u>ceaseless</u>. Its sound never stopped.

3. The <u>fierceness</u> of the Navajo Marines was well known. They were strong, brave, and powerful.

4. John felt <u>anxiety</u> about moving to Minnesota. He was nervous about living in a new place and worried about leaving.

5. Grandfather said that the code was a <u>triumph</u>. Each message was sent and received with success. Their goal had been reached!

6. Jen explained that only Navajos live on the <u>reservation</u>. The land is theirs to farm, protect, and enjoy.

7. Grandfather's face <u>wrinkled</u> as he laughed with his grandson. His cheeks scrunched up and lines appeared at the corners of his eyes.

8. When no rain fell, the leaves of Maria's favorite tree began to <u>wither</u>. They started to dry up and shrink.

© Macmillan/McGraw-Hill

At Home: Choose four of the above words and use each in an original sentence that uses context clues.

Suffixes are word parts that are added to the end of words to change their meanings. When added to base words, the **suffixes** *-less* and *-ness* are unaccented syllables. They receive less stress than the base words.

Example: fond + *-ness* = fondness. **Fond** is the accented syllable, not the suffix *-ness*.

Remember the suffix *-less* means "without." The suffix *-ness* means "the state or act of."

For each word listed in the table below, write the meaning and the accented syllable. Write the accented syllable in capital letters. Follow the example below.

Base word + suffix	Meaning	Accented syllable
Example: fearless	without fear, brave	FEAR less
effortless		
fierceness		
stillness		
forgiveness		
meaningless		
harmless		
weakness		
weightlessness		
motionless		
gladness		

At Home: Add four more words to the table above. Write their meanings and their accented syllables.

© Macmillan/McGraw-Hill

| attraction | emerged | inquire | focused |

A. Replace the underlined word or words in each sentence with a vocabulary word from the box.

1. We <u>concentrated</u> on the waves and nothing else, hoping to see a whale.

   _____

2. The immense blue whale finally <u>rose into view</u> from the water.

   _____

3. If you <u>ask</u> at the library, the librarians can provide several books about whales. _____

4. The beautiful harbor was the town's greatest <u>draw</u> for tourists.

   _____

B. Read each sentence below. Choose the correct meaning of the underlined word. Circle the letter of your answer.

5. The villagers had many <u>discussions</u> before they decided on a plan.

   a. conversations   **b.** problems   **c.** parties

6. The sleeping adult seals were <u>sprawled</u> across the beach as their pups played in the surf.

   a. in motion   **b.** awake and watchful   **c.** lying with limbs spread out

7. When she was frightened, the young child became <u>unreasonable</u> and wouldn't listen to her parents.

   a. foolish and senseless   **b.** happy and cheerful   **c.** easily distracted

8. After the scientists assured them that it was safe to do so, they <u>ventured</u> to touch the whale.

   a. feared   **b.** dared   **c.** planned

Name _____

When you **summarize,** you briefly restate or describe the main characters and most important events in a story.

Write a summary of each passage on the lines provided.

Ana Rosa sat down on her usual branch. Then she stared at the sea. She looked so hard and for so long that its blueness filled up her eyeballs, and she had to blink a lot so she wouldn't go blind.

The evening came and the sea's blueness turned gray. She watched and waited. Her stomach made grumbling noises but she muffled them with her hand.

Then, just as she began to think that maybe she had imagined it after all, she saw a splash of water rise up until it was high in the air.

_____

_____

_____

_____

Then everyone watched Ana Rosa and waited. She stood there trembling, holding that notebook with her story. She knew right then that this was it. The whole world would find out about her.

She stopped thinking. She just started to read. She read and read until she turned to the last page of the story. There the other sea creatures invite the lonely sea monster to a big underwater fiesta.

_____

_____

_____

_____

At Home: Read a short story or newspaper article. Summarize what you read in three sentences or less.

As you read *The Gri Gri Tree*, fill in the Summary Chart.

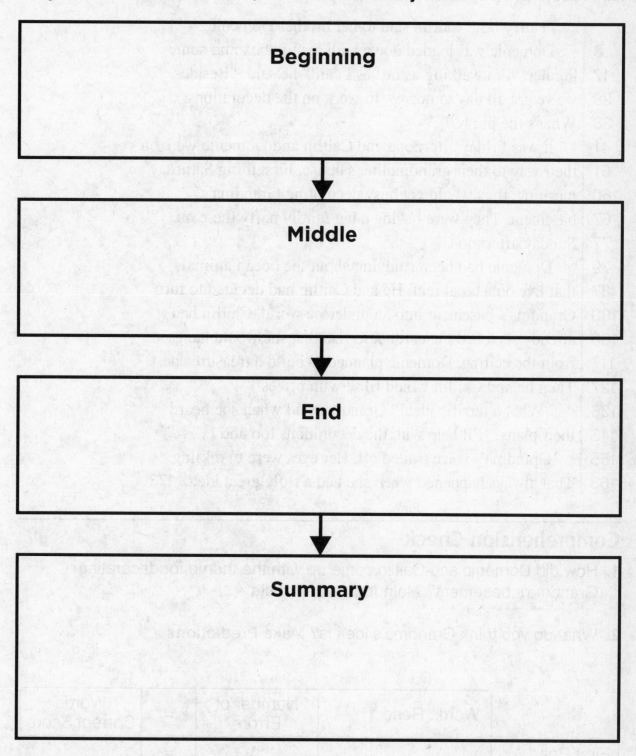

Beginning

↓

Middle

↓

End

↓

Summary

How does the information you wrote in this Summary Chart help you generate questions about *The Gri Gri Tree*?

 At Home: Have the student use the chart to retell the story.

Name _____

As I read, I will pay attention to tempo.

	"Hurry up!" Caitlin said to her brother Domenic.
8	Domenic was loaded down with his toolbox and some
17	lumber. "I'm walking as fast as I can!" he said. "Besides,
28	we've got all day tomorrow to work on the decorations.
38	What's the hurry?"
41	It was Friday afternoon and Caitlin and Domenic were on
51	their way to their grandmother's house. First thing Saturday
60	morning, they would get busy decorating Grandma's
67	basement. They were having a big family party there on
77	Sunday afternoon.
79	Domenic had been studying about the ocean animals
87	that live on a coral reef. He and Caitlin had decided to turn
100	Grandma's basement into an undersea world. Caitlin had
108	already sketched the cardboard fish that she would hang
117	from the ceiling. Domenic planned to build a treasure chest.
127	Then he and Caitlin would fill it with prizes.
136	"What a terrific idea!" Grandma said when she heard
145	their plans. "I'll help with the decorations too and I . . . ."
155	Grandma's voice trailed off. Her eyes were twinkling.
163	That always happened when she had a truly great idea. 173

Comprehension Check

1. How did Domenic and Caitlin come up with the theme for decorating Grandma's basement? **Main Idea and Details**

2. What do you think Grandma's idea is? **Make Predictions**

	Words Read	−	Number of Errors	=	Words Correct Score
First Read		−		=	
Second Read		−		=	

© Macmillan/McGraw-Hill

At Home: Help the student read the passage, paying attention to the goal at the top of the page.

A line **graph** shows how data changes over time.

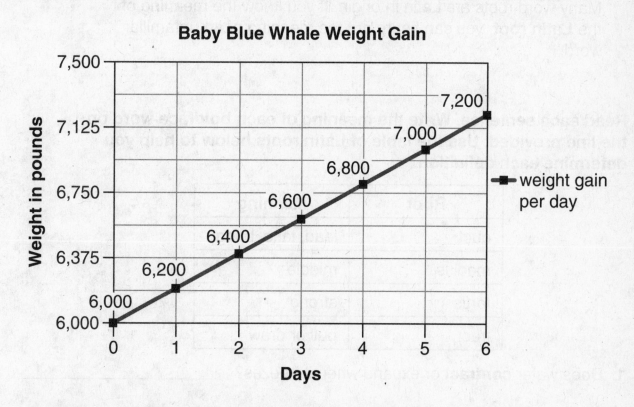

Baby Blue Whale Weight Gain

The graph above shows the weight gain of the blue whales for one week. Use the graph to answer the questions below.

1. What is the title of this graph?

_____

2. How much does the blue whale weigh on the first day?

_____

3. How much weight does a blue whale gain per day? _____

4. How much will a blue whale weigh on day 7? How did you get your answer?

_____

_____

_____

© Macmillan/McGraw-Hill

🏠 **At Home:** Use the information on the graph to write a short
description of a blue whale.

Name _____

A word root is part of a word that does not usually stand by itself as a base word. Prefixes or suffixes are attached to a word root. Many word roots are Latin in origin. If you know the meaning of the **Latin root**, you can figure out the meaning of an unfamiliar word.

Read each sentence. Write the meaning of each boldface word on the line provided. Use the table of Latin roots below to help you determine each definition.

Root	Meaning
duct	lead, take, bring
medius	middle
fortis	strong
tract	pull or draw

1. Does water **contract** or expand when it freezes? _____

_____

2. The boys could not agree, so a **mediator** was called in to hear both

arguments. _____

_____

3. The **aqueducts** brought water into the ancient city. _____

_____

4. Let's make a **deduction** based on the facts we know. _____

_____

5. The troops **fortified** the town in preparation for the enemy invasion.

_____

© Macmillan/McGraw-Hill

At Home: The Latin word root *hab* means "hold." Find or think of two words that contain this word root. Write the definition of each word.

The suffix **-ion** means "act or process," or "state or condition." You must drop the **e** from words that end in silent **e** before adding **-ion**. For example, the word **separate** must lose its **e** before you can add **-ion** to make the word **separation**.

Add -ion to the words in the box to complete each sentence below. Remember to drop the silent e before adding -ion.

concentrate	exhaust	confuse	discuss
elect	decorate	correct	locate

1. The results of the _____ showed that the more experienced candidate won the most votes.

2. The incomplete directions led to _____ among the students.

3. They used the roses as _____ on the parade float.

4. He was so focused during the test that nothing could break his _____.

5. Staying up late can lead to _____ if you do not get enough sleep.

6. Although the _____ of the park was marked on the map, she could not find it.

7. The student worked very hard on his paper, and it needed only one small _____.

8. When they could not agree, their _____ quickly became an argument.

At Home: List at least eight more words that have -ion endings.

The Gri Gri Tree • Grade 5/Unit 5 183

© Macmillan/McGraw-Hill

A. Complete each sentence with the correct vocabulary word from the box.

> discussions   inquire   labor   abandon   uninhabited

1. People do not live in _____ places like Antarctica.

2. The construction workers were tired from the hard _____ of building a skyscraper.

3. The members of the tribe stayed up very late to have serious _____ about the future.

4. We had to _____ the ship when it began to sink.

5. It is important to _____ about directions to the campsite.

B. Write the vocabulary word from the box that means almost the same as the underlined word or words.

> treacherous   dismantled   traditional   unreasonable   frigid

6. It was <u>freezing</u> _____ in the unheated house.

7. My father <u>took apart</u> _____ the vacuum cleaner to find out what was wrong with it.

8. It is <u>customary</u> _____ for my family to have turkey for Thanksgiving dinner.

9. Climbing up a steep mountain can be very <u>dangerous</u> _____.

10. The two men would not stop arguing about which road to take; they were being <u>very difficult to reason with</u> _____.

© Macmillan/McGraw-Hill

A. Use each of the vocabulary words in the box to write a sentence.

combined	vacant	shield	attraction	shortage	strategy

1. _____
_____

2. _____
_____

3. _____
_____

4. _____
_____

5. _____
_____

6. _____
_____

B. Match each word in column 1 with its antonym in column 2. Write the letter of the correct word from column 2 on the line.

Column 1

7. peace _____

8. failure _____

9. straight _____

10. member _____

11. simple _____

12. hidden _____

Column 2

a. emerged

b. outcast

c. complex

d. bedlam

e. creased

f. triumph

Name _____

A. **Select the correct word from the choices in parentheses.**
   Then write the correct word on the line provided.

1. The princess (descended / described) the stairs to meet the prince

   in the hall. _____

2. No princess was willing to (autograph / accompany) Prince Vincent

   down the aisle. _____

3. If the prince did not marry, the king would (despair / dismiss) him from

   the kingdom. _____

4. Prince Vincent was in (despair / delight), and his future looked hopeless.

   _____

5. The horse's (huntsman / bridle) was broken, and the harness would not fit.

   _____

6. The queen welcomed the princess as her guest and served her

   (delicacies / intentions) from different nations. _____

7. The prince told the queen about his (decorations / intentions) to marry

   the princess. _____

8. The princess (dismissed / consented) to his proposal, and they lived

   happily ever after. _____

B. **Use two vocabulary words to write a sentence for each. Then**
   underline the vocabulary word.

9. _____

   _____

10. _____

    _____

Name _____

The **sequence** of events is the order in which things happen in a story. Determining the sequence of events can help you summarize the action of a story.

Place the correct number for the sequence of events in the left column next to the event described in the right column.

After Alexi spared the life of the Golden Mare, the horse became devoted to Alexi. Alexi became a huntsman for the Tsar. As his first order of business, Alexi captured the Firebird. Next, he asked Alexi to find Yelena the Fair so she could become his wife. Alexi persuaded Yelena to meet the Tsar. After Yelena discovered the Tsar's intention, she told the Tsar she would not get married without her grandmother's ring. The Golden Mare volunteered to fetch the ring from the lake. Yelena convinced the Tsar that she would turn a pot of water into a fountain of youth for him. The Tsar decided to test the water by having Alexi thrown in. Alexi survived and came out of the water with the ring. The Tsar was convinced that his youth would be restored but he became an infant instead. Since he was too young to rule, Alexi became the Tsar and married Yelena. Alexi released the Firebird and the Golden Mare.

Order	Events from *The Golden Mare, the Firebird, and the Magic Ring*
	Alexi becomes a huntsman for the Tsar and captures the Firebird.
	Alexi spares the life of the Golden Mare, and the horse devotes her life to him.
	Yelena follows Alexi to meet the Tsar.
	Alexi is thrown into the cauldron of boiling water and survives.
	Alexi becomes Tsar and releases the Golden Mare.
	The Golden Mare volunteers to fetch Yelena's magic ring.

© Macmillan/McGraw-Hill

At Home: Make a story chart for events that happened to you yesterday.

Name _____

As you read *The Golden Mare, the Firebird, and the Magic Ring*, fill
in the Sequence Chart.

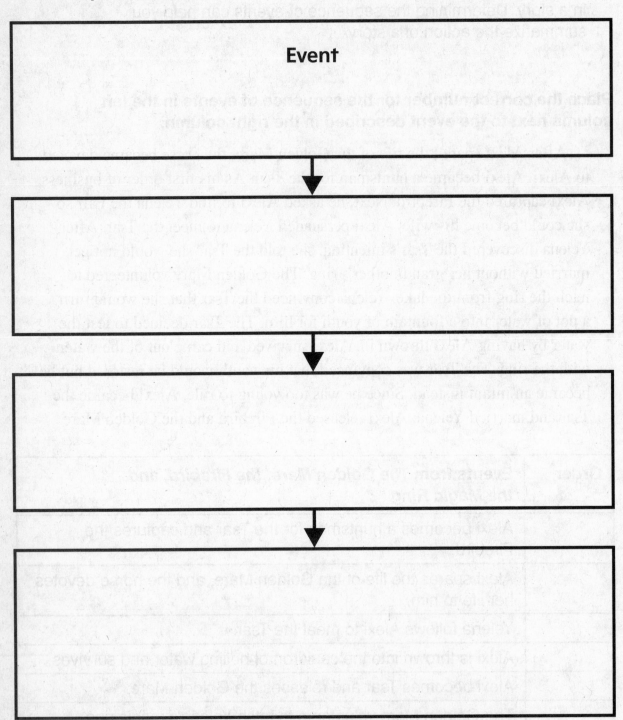

Event

How does the information you wrote in this Sequence Chart help you
summarize *The Golden Mare, the Firebird, and the Magic Ring*?

At Home: Have the student use the chart to retell the story.

As I read, I will pay attention to pauses and intonation.

	Once upon a time, a really, really long time ago, there lived
12	a beautiful, kind-hearted girl named Katharine. You would
21	have thought that such a lovely girl would be happy. But she
33	was not. She was sad and terribly lonely.
41	For you see (as is to be expected in a story like this),
54	Katharine's life was filled with sorrow. Her mother died
63	when she was young. Her father brought her to live with her
75	Aunt Mara and cousins Melina and Ursula while he went off
86	to fight for the king. Her father loved Katharine dearly and
97	promised to return for her as soon as possible, but that
108	promise was made many years ago.
114	Over the years Katharine's cousins grew to hate her. They
124	knew that Katharine was kinder and more beautiful than they
134	were. Each day Melina and Ursula were meaner. They
143	ordered her around. Katharine was truly miserable.
150	So what did Katharine do all day? She did everything!
160	Inside she cooked and cleaned. Outside she planted, weeded,
169	and harvested the garden, fed the animals, cleaned the barn,
179	collected the eggs, and milked the cow. 186

Comprehension Check

1. Why was Katharine miserable? **Plot**

2. Why were Ursula and Melina cruel to Katharine? **Make Inferences**

	Words Read	–	Number of Errors	=	Words Correct Score
First Read		–		=	
Second Read		–		=	

At Home: Help the student read the passage, paying attention to the goal at the type of the page.

The Golden Mare, the Firebird, and the Magic Ring • Grade 5/Unit 6

189

© Macmillan/McGraw-Hill

Name _____

A **Venn diagram** compares two things. Differences are written in the left and right circles. Similarities are written where the circles overlap.

A. Read the summary of *Cinderella* and fill in the Venn diagram.

Cinderella

Cinderella is a household servant with an evil stepmother, evil stepsisters, and a fairy godmother. She loses a slipper at a ball, and the prince searches the kingdom for the woman to whom it belongs. Cinderella and the prince get married and live happily ever after.

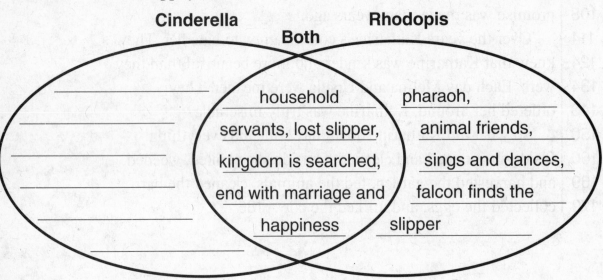

Cinderella   **Both**   **Rhodopis**

household servants, lost slipper, kingdom is searched, end with marriage and happiness

pharaoh, animal friends, sings and dances, falcon finds the slipper

B. Read the completed Venn diagram and write a summary of *Rhodopis*.

Rhodopis

_____

_____

_____

_____

_____

_____

At Home: Use a Venn diagram to compare yourself to a friend or family member.

© Macmillan/McGraw-Hill

Homophones are words that sound the same but have different spellings and different meanings.

A. Circle the word that makes sense in each sentence.

1. Most fairy tales are stories that you have (herd / heard) before.

2. The hero often must race to complete a task in just one (hour / our).

3. In some stories, people try to (by / buy) happiness with jewels or gold.

4. My baseball team (one / won) the game.

B. Write a word from the box next to each word to make pairs of homophones, and write a sentence using one of the homophones in the pair.

pear	flower	course	hear

5. here _____

_____

6. coarse _____

_____

7. pair _____

_____

8. flour _____

_____

At Home: List three additional pairs of homophones. Choose three words, and correctly use each one in a sentence.

The Golden Mare, the Firebird, and
the Magic Ring • **Grade 5/Unit 6**

191

Name _____

Many words are Greek in origin. Word roots are small word parts that usually cannot stand on their own. Knowing the meanings of **Greek roots** can help you define unfamiliar words.

Read the table. Then write the correct word from the box below to complete each sentence.

Greek root	Meaning	Example
astr	star	astronaut
auto	self, same	automatic
photo	light	photogenic
mech	machine	mechanism
graph	thing written	graphic
phon	sound, voice	phonetic

photocopy	astronomer	automobile
biography	mechanic	phonics

1. The vehicle needed a _____ who knew how its engine worked.

2. We studied sounds and syllables in our _____ class.

3. Ms. Brown made one more _____ of the worksheet for the new student.

4. The author wrote a _____ about Harriet Tubman.

5. Thanks to the _____ , we don't have to walk to school.

6. An _____ looked at the stars through her telescope.

At Home: Read a newspaper or magazine, and find three words that include Greek roots. Then use each word in a sentence.

© Macmillan/McGraw-Hill

Name _____

A. Match the vocabulary word with its definition. Then write the letter of the correct word on the line.

1. ease _____   **a.** joined together

2. scenery _____   **b.** disappointed or kept from doing something

3. bundle _____   **c.** working well together

4. fused _____   **d.** move carefully or slowly

5. guaranteed _____   **e.** landscape

6. supervise _____   **f.** group of things held together

7. frustrated _____   **g.** assured

8. coordination _____ **h.** watch and direct

B. Fill in the paragraph using the eight vocabulary words from section A.

My uncle _____ that we would enjoy the _____ of the mountains and lake. But the trip did not start out great. We tried to _____ the tent out of the stuffed car, but it wouldn't budge. Next, my older brother became _____ when he noticed the _____ of hamburgers was _____ together. Unfortunately, we did not bring any other food for dinner. We relied on the _____ of all three of us to get the hamburgers separated. While my uncle cooked, he wanted to _____ me as I unpacked the rest of the car. I was about to ask to go home when I saw two baby deer playing with each other. I guess being in nature is worth a frozen dinner and over-stuffed car.

Name _____

When you read a story, you **make judgments** about the characters and the things they say or do. You might make a judgment about whether a character made a good choice or a poor choice.

Answer each question below. Then explain your answers.

1. It takes Uncle Curtis three tries to find the exit to Mount Tamalpais. When Uncle Curtis finally makes it to the park, he is given a map of the campgrounds. He "didn't even glance at it but threw it into the backseat." Do you think he made a wise decision when he chose to ignore the map?

    _____

    _____

    _____

2. Teddy and Bobby wear clothes appropriate for a San Francisco summer—sweatshirts and corduroys. The weather forecast for Mount Tamalpais is hot and humid. Teddy and Bobby decide to pack only sweatshirts and corduroys to take to the camp. What do you think of their clothing decision?

    _____

    _____

    _____

3. Teddy and Bobby find that the hot dogs and hamburgers, which Teddy had packed in dry ice, are frozen solid. But Uncle Curtis tries to grill the frozen food before it has thawed. Do you think that Teddy's method of packing the meat was successful?

    _____

    _____

    _____

© Macmillan/McGraw-Hill

At Home: Choose a character from a story who behaves most like you. Then make a judgment about one thing that character does and explain your opinion.

As you read *Skunk Scout*, fill in the Judgments Chart.

Action		Judgment
	→	
	→	
	→	
	→	

How does the information you wrote in this Judgments Chart help you monitor comprehension of *Skunk Scout*?

© Macmillan/McGraw-Hill

At Home: Have the student use the chart to retell the story.

Skunk Scout • Grade 5/Unit 6 |195|

Name _____

As I read, I will pay attention to punctuation and inflection.

	Can you guess what main force created the Grand
9	Canyon? It was the mighty Colorado River.
16	The Colorado is a huge, powerful river. In the spring,
26	melted snow fills the river, and it becomes swift and wild.
37	The river picks up rocks, huge boulders, sand, and pebbles
47	and carries them along. Over millions of years, this gritty
57	river water carved into layer after layer of rock. It carved the
69	deepest canyon of all, the Grand Canyon.
76	One reason the river could carve the rock is that the rock
88	was soft. Soft for rock, that is! Back in time, before there was
101	a Grand Canyon, oceans covered the land.
108	Over millions of years, broken seashells, sand, mud, and
117	clay fell to the bottom of the sea. These small bits of matter
130	that settle on the sea bottom are called sediment. Over
140	millions of years, the sediment turned into rock, called
149	sedimentary rock. And this rock was soft enough for the river
160	to be able to carve a deeper and deeper path through it.
172	But the Colorado River was not the only force to form the
184	Grand Canyon. 186

Comprehension Check

1. How did the Colorado River help form the Grand Canyon? **Main Idea and Details**

2. What is sedimentary rock? **Main Idea and Details**

	Words Read	–	Number of Errors	=	Words Correct Score
First Read		–		=	
Second Read		–		=	

© Macmillan/McGraw-Hill

At Home: Help the student read the passage, paying attention to the goal at the top of the page.

An **interview** is a way to gain information from someone. When you conduct an interview, you ask a person questions and he or she provides answers.

Read the interview of park ranger, Dan Levitt. Then answer the questions.

Reporter: What are the kinds of things you have to do when you are a park ranger?

Dan: There really is no typical day. We do a lot of different things. We do campfire presentations where we show photos and read a narrative. I'm doing one on the Rio Grande and its water quality. We talk about water, the earth, and plants and animals found here in the park. We also tend to the park trails and operate visitor centers.

Reporter: What did you study to become a park ranger?

Dan: I have a bachelor's degree in geography, but you can study anything from geology to paleontology. I got my start by volunteering at various parks. Here I find that I use all the science courses I've taken.

1. What kinds of work do park rangers do? _____

_____

2. What could a person study to become a park ranger?

_____

_____

3. What could the reporter ask Dan if he or she wanted to learn more about

campfire presentations? _____

_____

4. If you were the reporter, what question would you ask Dan?

_____

_____

At Home: Interview a friend or family member. Ask five questions, and write a summary based on his or her responses.

Words with more than one meaning are **multiple-meaning words.** You can use context clues, or other words in the sentence, to help you figure out the meaning. Sometimes you must use a dictionary to learn the different meanings of the word.

A. Read each sentence. Then circle the letter next to the correct meaning of each underlined word.

1. My first camping trip <u>might</u> have been a disaster, but it turned out great.

   a. physical strength   **b.** expressing possibility or doubt

2. We had to change a flat tire on the way to the campground, but the <u>spare</u> tire worked fine.

   a. extra   **b.** hold back or avoid

3. After that we set up our tent near some trees and <u>brush</u>.

   a. object with bristles on a handle   **b.** heavy growth of bushes

4. <u>Cavities</u> in the rocks near the river were the perfect place to store our towels while we swam in the lake.

   a. hollow places   **b.** decayed spots on teeth

5. He still had some <u>change</u> in his pocket.

   a. to become different   **b.** coins

6. As the day came to a <u>close</u>, I was happy to be camping.

   a. end   **b.** shut

B. Use a dictionary to find two meanings of each multiple-meaning word listed below.

7. jam   **a.** _____

             b. _____

8. coat   **a.** _____

             b. _____

© Macmillan/McGraw-Hill

At Home: Write a paragraph containing ten multiple-meaning words. Write at least three sentences using each meaning of each word.

Name _____

Many words in English have **Latin roots.** You can define unfamiliar words by recognizing a Latin root and using context clues.

Latin Roots	Meaning
aud	to hear
tract	to drag, draw
port	to carry
spect	to look
mit/miss	to send

Read the root chart and write the root of each underlined word in the sentences below. Then use context clues and the meaning of the Latin roots to write a definition of each underlined word.

1. Making a campfire is tricky. First an adult must <u>transport</u> wood

   to your campsite. _____ *Transport* means _____.

2. Then you must <u>inspect</u> the wood to make sure that it is dry. _____

   Inspect means _____.

3. When an adult lights the fire, you will notice an <u>audible</u> *crackle* and *pop* as

   the wood begins to burn. _____ *Audible* means _____

   _____.

4. The <u>spectacle</u> of a roaring fire is a wonderful sight. _____

   Spectacle means _____.

5. For some people, the main <u>attraction</u> of a campfire is roasting

   marshmallows. _____ *Attraction* means _____

   _____.

At Home: Read a magazine, newspaper, or a book and find as many Latin root words as you can.

Skunk Scout • Grade 5/Unit 6   **199**

© Macmillan/McGraw-Hill

Name _____

A. Match the words with their definitions. Then write the letter on the line.

1. rigid _____   **a.** of or relating to the body

2. wheelchair _____   **b.** not yielding or bending

3. interact _____   **c.** simple or basic

4. physical _____   **d.** a chair mounted on wheels

5. elementary _____   **e.** to act on or influence each other

B. Choose the word in parentheses that will complete each sentence. Then write the word on the line.

6. Children should learn (physical, rigid) activities that they will still enjoy

   when they are adults. _____

7. Sports that allow you to (salute, interact) with the natural environment are

   exciting. _____

8. The team followed a (rigid, gracious) exercise routine that involved running
   a mile, 100 push-ups, and jumping rope everyday.

   _____

9. A person in a (parasol, wheelchair) can compete in the Paralympics.

   _____

10. Pete was new to sailing, so he took an (elementary, diverse) sailing class

    to learn more. _____

C. Find the vocabulary words in the word search below.

11. j u w o i c s p h y s i c a l l k j

12. a k j e l e m e n t a r y u e u y p

13. r i g y i u o w h e e l c h a i r z

14. a r l r i g i d l k j j f i n t e r

Name _____

You encounter techniques of **persuasion** every day. Persuasion is communication meant to convince you that you should believe something, act in a certain way, or participate in something. People trying to persuade you can use a variety of techniques.

Techniques of Persuasion
Testimonial: a statement of support by a noteworthy person
Bandwagon: The product or activity is said to be popular with everyone.
Emotional appeal: Language is used to make a person feel strong emotions.
Repetition: a name being repeated many times
Slogan: a catchy phrase

Match a technique of persuasion to each example.

1. Our wheelchairs are used nationwide by all Paralympians everywhere.

   _____

2. Boundless Playgrounds are fun! Boundless Playgrounds are safe!

   Boundless Playgrounds make memories! _____

3. A GPS device in your hands makes your feet "Glad to Walk Positively

   Anywhere Safely." _____

4. Hi, I'm proud to use FastBreak Wheelchairs. Because of FastBreak Wheelchairs, I was named one of the top young athletes in the nation.

   _____

5. Would you enjoy never going anywhere new, never hearing new sounds, and never meeting new people? Probably not. With GPS, you can be free to walk anywhere, any way, and any time that you want!

   _____

© Macmillan/McGraw-Hill

At Home: Find three examples of persuasion in a newspaper or magazine.

A Dream Comes True
Grade 5/Unit 6

201

As you read "A Dream Comes True", fill in the Fact and Opinion Chart.

Fact	Opinion

How does the information you wrote in this Fact and Opinion Chart help
you monitor comprehension of "A Dream Comes True"?

At Home: Have the student use the chart to retell the story.

© Macmillan/McGraw-Hill

As I read, I will pay attention to pronunciation.

7	**Wheelchair** basketball is probably the oldest competitive
	wheelchair sport. It began after World War II as a way to get
19	disabled veterans active. Now children ages 6 and up are
28	playing wheelchair basketball in gyms everywhere. They
35	play on the same size court and use most of the same rules as
49	their classmates. And they're getting a lot of exercise, too.
59	Only a few rules are adapted in wheelchair basketball.
68	For example, if a player takes more than two pushes of the
80	wheelchair while dribbling, a traveling penalty is called. Even
89	if only the wheel of a player's wheelchair goes out of bounds,
101	the player is out of bounds. A player who lifts out of his or her
116	seat to get a **physical** advantage gets charged with a foul. So
128	does a player whose feet touch the floor.
136	Like wheelchair hockey, each wheelchair basketball player
143	is classified according to his or her ability level.
152	Wheelchair basketball, like wheelchair hockey, takes
158	coordination. Players must use their hands to move their
167	wheelchairs. At the same time, they must be able to handle
178	the ball. 180

Comprehension Check

1. Why does wheelchair basketball take coordination? **Main Idea and Details**

2. Why is it important to adapt sports? **Draw Conclusions**

	Words Read	–	Number of Errors	=	Words Correct Score
First Read		–		=	
Second Read		–		=	

© Macmillan/McGraw-Hill

At Home: Help the student read the passage, paying attention to the goal at the top of the page.

A Dream Comes True
Grade 5/Unit 6   **203**

You see printed materials every day that provide information about the world around you. **Everyday communications** have many forms.

Study the descriptions below. Then answer the questions.

Consumer materials	Warranty: guarantees a product or its parts for a period of time
	Product instructions: explain how to operate a product
Directions	Maps explain how to get from one place to another.
Advertisements	Help-wanted ad: explains a particular job and how to apply for it
	Store ad: provides information about the store and its merchandise
Brochure	a small booklet that contains information about a place, service, person, or object
Newsletter	a printed report or letter giving information about a special group or organization

1. What might you read if you were looking for a job? _____

2. Would you read a brochure or a warranty to learn more about a museum

   exhibit? _____

3. A neighborhood club is planning a Fourth of July parade. What would you

   read to find out when and where the parade begins? _____

4. What might you read to learn how to operate your new camera?

   _____

5. What would you use to get directions from California to Texas?

   _____

At Home: List three examples of everyday communications that you can find in your home.

> You can figure out the meaning of an unfamiliar word by using
> **context clues**, the words around the unfamiliar word.

Read each sentence. Use context clues to help you define the boldface word. Then write the letter of the best choice on the line.

1. During the game my **opponent** was the best player on the other team.

   An opponent is _____.

   a. a competitor   **b.** an ally   **c.** a coach

2. The athletes trained at a high **altitude** because it is much more difficult to run in the mountains.

   Altitude is _____.

   a. an underwater cave   **b.** the height above sea level   **c.** a plateau

3. The winning women's basketball team looked **regal** with their gold medals and flowers on top of the podium.

   Regal means _____.

   a. deprived of food   **b.** serious   **c.** like royalty

4. Joe was accompanied by his guide dog, who **escorted** him into the gymnasium.

   To be escorted is to be _____.

   a. complex   **b.** guided   **c.** called

5. For months the team practiced their **maneuvers** until the exercises became natural to them.

   Maneuvers are _____.

   a. movements   **b.** schedules   **c.** relationships

At Home: Find an unfamiliar word in a favorite story. Then make a poster that explains the word with context clues.

The names of characters from Greek and Roman mythology are origins of many English words. Recognizing **words from mythology** can help you figure out the meanings of unfamiliar words.

A. Match each word to the name from Greek or Roman mythology that best explains each word's origin. Then write the letter of the name on the line.

1. fortune _____

2. cosmic _____

3. titanic _____

4. volcano _____

5. cereal _____

6. jovial _____

7. geology _____

8. furious _____

9. January _____

10. Olympics _____

   a. Jove, the Roman god who controlled the weather

   b. Fortuna, the Roman goddess of luck

   c. Gaea, the Greek Earth goddess

   d. Furies, angry spirits in Greek mythology

   e. Janus, the Roman god of beginnings

   f. Cosmos, the Greek word for *universe*

   g. Mount Olympus, the home of the gods in Greek mythology

   h. Titans, Greek giants who had enormous strength

   i. Ceres, the Roman goddess of grain

   j. Vulcan, the Roman god of fire

B. Use four words from the first column to make two sentences.

11. _____

_____

12. _____

_____

At Home: Look for three more words that originate from Greek and Roman mythology.

Name _____

| launched | particles | dense | inflate |
| anchored | hydrogen | scientific | companion |

A. Choose the word from the list above that best completes each sentence. Then write the word on the line.

1. The hot-air balloon soared through the air because it was not

   _____, or held down, to the ground by anything.

2. The balloons soar because the hot-air is light and the air surrounding

   it is heavy and _____.

3. People in hot-air balloons are _____ into the sky.

4. The large balloons _____ when they are filled with hot air.

5. The small pieces of matter in air move faster as the air heats. Then the

   _____ spread out, and the balloon rises.

6. _____ is a gas that is lighter than air, so it also can be
   used in hot-air balloons.

7. Some people ride in hot-air balloons to do _____ experiments.

8. You and a _____ might enjoy sharing a hot-air balloon ride.

B. Label the statements True or False.

9. The science club launched the balloon, and it dug deep into the earth.

   _____

10. You can inflate a balloon with hydrogen or hot air. _____

11. The balloon will not move when it is anchored to the ground.

   _____

12. To conduct scientific experiments you must bring a companion.

   _____

When you **make generalizations,** you state a broad idea that describes the information in a passage. You combine what you already know with information in the text to form a general statement about a topic or an idea.

Read the pairs of sentences. Then form a generalization based on each set of statements below.

1. Today there are no clouds, no storms, and no high winds. It is a perfect day for ballooning.

   _____

   _____

2. Thousands of people belong to hot-air balloon clubs. People from different parts of the world like ballooning.

   _____

   _____

3. Joseph Montgolfier noticed that hot air rises. He and his brother built the

   first hot-air balloon. _____

   _____

4. Early hot-air balloons flew very high. Early hot-air balloons carried no people.

   _____

   _____

5. The first public balloon flight was in France. A Frenchman was the first

   person to ride in a balloon. _____

   _____

At Home: Draw a diagram of a hot-air balloon. Then write a paragraph making generalizations about its parts and how it rises.

Name _____

As you read *Up in the Air: The Story of Balloon Flight,* fill in the
Generalizations Chart.

Information from Text	
Prior Knowledge	
Generalizations	

How does the information you wrote in the Generalizations Chart help
you monitor comprehension of *Up in the Air*?

 At Home: Have the student use the chart to retell the story.

As I read, I will pay attention to tempo and phrasing.

	It is a beautiful day at the football stadium. Fans fill the
12	seats and wait for the kickoff. Suddenly, a strange shadow
22	appears on the field. People sitting in the upper rows hear
33	a low whirring sound overhead. Floating in the sky is a
44	football-shaped balloon.
47	Most of us have seen them on television during sporting
57	events. They are like silent ships sailing on a sea of sky.
69	These strange-looking balloons are called blimps. They are
77	cousins to the hot-air balloon.
82	Blimps and hot-air balloons are part of a group of flying
93	machines known as lighter-than-air craft. They are filled
101	with gas that weighs less than air.
108	Blimps are also members of the airship family. Just like
118	boats, airships have motors and rudders. The motors give
127	airships speed. The rudders help steer. This makes airships
136	very different from hot-air balloons. Hot-air balloons have
144	little control over their speed or direction. Airships can even
154	fly against the wind. 158

Comprehension Check

1. Compare and contrast blimps and hot-air balloons. **Compare and Contrast**

2. Where do people commonly see blimps? **Main Idea and Details**

	Words Read	–	Number of Errors	=	Words Correct Score
First Read		–		=	
Second Read		–		=	

© Macmillan/McGraw-Hill

At Home: Help the student read the passage, paying attention to the goal at the top of the page.

When you read poetry, you often encounter poetic elements such as **similes** and **metaphors.** Similes and metaphors use language to create striking or unexpected images for the reader. These are figures of speech that compare or associate two things. Similes use *like* or *as* in the comparison. Metaphors do not use *like* or *as.*

Read the poem to answer the following questions.

Balloon Flight Haiku

It floats in the air
Like a bird's loosened feather,
drifting among blue.

The azure ocean
above our very heads
is where it sails high.

Unlike a feather,
it is guided by someone
who chooses its course.

1. What similes can you find in the haiku?

_____

2. What metaphors can you find in the haiku?

_____

3. What comparisons are made in the haiku?

_____
_____

4. Which comparison is not stated directly? How do you know the comparison is made?

_____
_____

At Home: Write several similes and metaphors that describe
a hot-air balloon flying in the sky.

Many English words have roots that originally came from the ancient Greek language. Knowing what the **Greek root** means will help you figure out the meaning of the word.

Root	Meaning
hydro	water
aster/astro	star
dem	people
graph	write
log/logue	word
pod	foot

Use the chart above to help you choose which word is being described in each item below.

1. The lightest gas, this element is found in water and all organic substances.

   (helium, hydrogen) _____

2. This is a noun that means "a conversation, often in a story."

   (dialogue, dialect) _____

3. This object has three "feet." (tricycle, tripod) _____

4. This kind of political system allows the people to vote for their government.

   (democracy, monarchy) _____

5. This is a form of communication that people use to write in Morse code.

   (telephone, telegraph) _____

6. This is the study of the stars and planets. (geology, astronomy)

   _____

At Home: Choose five of the words above and write sentences using them.

Name _____

Prefixes are word parts added to the beginning of other words or word parts. A prefix changes the word's meaning. Some prefixes refer to an amount and are called **number prefixes**.

prefix	number	example
uni-	1	unity
bi-	2	bicycle
tri-	3	triceratops
cent-	100	centennial

A. Choose the best prefix for the boldface word. Then write the complete word on the line.

1. The girl put on her soccer _____**form** before the game.

   _____

2. Every _____**meter** counts when carefully measuring the length of a board. _____

3. The _____**cycle** has three wheels. _____

4. Stephanie was _____**lingual** and knew two languages.

   _____

B. Circle the prefix in each word. Then write a definition of the word that is based on the meaning of the prefix.

5. triangle _____

6. universe _____

7. bisect _____

8. centipede _____

9. tripod _____

10. unicorn _____

© Macmillan/McGraw-Hill

At Home: Write a paragraph containing the five words with number prefixes.

Up in the Air • Grade 5/Unit 6   213

specimens	erupted	murky	dormant
biology	scoured	research	observer

Choose the word that best replaces the underlined word or words. Then write the word on the line.

1. If you are curious about <u>the study of living things,</u> you can make amazing discoveries. _____

2. First you must become <u>someone who watches everything around you</u>. _____

3. Your <u>investigations</u> might take you to a park or even to a lake, where you can study life under the water. _____

4. Sometimes a lake will look <u>as though it has no activity</u>, but it is really filled with life. _____

5. In the water you may find minerals to be <u>cleaned</u> back in the lab.

   _____

6. Even if the water is <u>thick and dark</u>, you will probably find something fascinating. _____

7. Take <u>samples</u> of the water so that you can study them under a microscope.

   _____

8. You may find evidence that a volcano <u>exploded</u> or evidence of other natural events in your water samples. _____

© Macmillan/McGraw-Hill

Name _____

> Events or steps usually happen in **sequence** or in a particular order. If you can recognize and follow the sequence, you will better understand what will happen next. Words such as *first*, *then*, *next*, *now*, and *finally* help signal the order in which events or steps occur.

Read the scientific method. Label each step of the scientific method below.

Scientific method is specific steps scientists take during an experiment. Scientists try to answer questions they have by performing several tests. By following a specific sequence during different experiments, they are able to determine the answers to their questions.

1. Initial or First Observation: Scientists notice something and wonder why.
2. Gather Information: Scientists try to find out more.
3. Hypothesis: Scientists take their initial observation and create a question that can be tested. A hypothesis should make a prediction of the outcome.
4. Testing: Scientists will perform experiments and record data.
5. Draw a Conclusion: Using the information from their tests, scientists will compare this data to their hypothesis to see if their prediction is correct or not.

1. Finally I conclude my hypothesis was correct. The birds made a nest to hold their eggs. _____

2. Then I learned more from a book about birds laying eggs in the spring.

   _____

3. First I see two blue birds. One is flying from tree to tree. The other is gathering twigs. It is springtime. _____

4. Next I observe the birds for a week. They choose a large tree branch. The birds gather more twigs and start building a nest. I see three bird eggs.

   _____

5. I predict the birds will make a nest to hold their eggs.

   _____

At Home: Write a paragraph explaining why it is important for scientists to follow a specific sequence.

As you read *Hidden Worlds* fill in the Sequence Chart.

Event

↓

↓

· ·

Event

↓

↓

© Macmillan/McGraw-Hill

How does the information you wrote in the Sequence Chart help you
summarize *Hidden Worlds*?

At Home: Have the student use the chart to retell the story.

As I read, I will pay attention to pauses and intonation.

	The ocean is big. It covers about two-thirds of Earth. The
11	ocean is also deep—very deep. The ocean's average depth is
22	more than 2 miles (3 kilometers). At its deepest it goes down
32	nearly 7 miles (11 kilometers). That's taller than Mount
39	Everest.
40	Think of a place where animals live. You might think of
51	a forest or grassland. But what about the ocean? In fact, the
63	ocean makes up most of Earth's habitat. But to this day, most
75	of the deep ocean has never been explored.
83	For centuries, people thought that the bottom of the deep
93	ocean was lifeless. It is very cold in the deep, dark ocean. No
106	light reaches the bottom. And water is heavy. All that water
117	presses down hard on the sea floor. How could anything live
128	down there?
130	But then scientists began exploring the deep. What they
139	found shocked them. On the deep sea floor, they discovered
149	a world beyond their wildest imagination. It is a strange
159	world teeming with bizarre life. 164

Comprehension Check

1. What is it like at the bottom of the ocean? **Main Idea and Details**

2. Why has not much of the deep ocean been explored? **Main Idea and Details**

	Words Read	–	Number of Errors	=	Words Correct Score
First Read		–		=	
Second Read		–		=	

At Home: Help the student read the passage, paying attention to the goal at the top of the page.

A myth is a traditional story that explains imaginary events from the past or a traditional world view. Myths describe how a custom, belief, or natural phenomenon came about. **Symbolism** is the use of concrete objects to represent abstract ideas or qualities. **Figurative language** uses imaginative language to describe objects, places, or people.

Read the myth below, then answer the questions.

A long time ago there was one land and one people. Everyone lived together happily and in peace. Then two brothers were born who quarreled over everything. This made the Creator angry. In a voice like low, rumbling thunder, he told the brothers to shoot an arrow into the air. Each brother and his people would live where his arrow landed.

Soon the brothers started quarreling again. Once more the Creator became angry. This time he took away fire from everyone except for one old woman called Loo-Wit. The people stopped quarreling, and the Creator asked Loo-Wit to share her fire. In return, the Creator offered to grant her one wish. She chose to be young and beautiful. When the two brothers saw how beautiful Loo-Wit was, each of them wanted to marry her. Again there was quarreling, which caused the Creator to turn each brother into a mountain and also to make Loo-Wit a mountain.

1. The myth says that the brothers shot their arrows into the air. What does

   this explain? _____

   _____

2. What do the mountains symbolize? _____

   _____

3. Find an example of figurative language in the myth.

   _____

   _____

At Home: Discuss with a parent or helper why people long ago used myths as a way of explaining their world.

Name _____

Many words in English have ancient **Latin or Greek word parts**. Sometimes Latin or Greek word parts create a word family, or a group of words with a common feature or pattern. For example, the Greek root *geo* means "earth." The words *geography, geology, geographer, geode, geometry,* and *geometric* form a word family based on the words' Greek root *geo*.

Origin	Greek	Latin	Greek	Latin	Latin
Word part	bio	dict	tele	man	terr
Meaning	life	speak	far away	hand	earth

Look at the Latin and Greek word parts above. Choose the word in parentheses that best fits with the other two words to form a word family. Then write the word on the line.

1. bionic   biography   (biosphere/bicker) _____

2. dictate   dictation   (dice/dictionary) _____

3. telethon   telephone   (telescope/territory) _____

4. manner   maneuver   (manicure/main) _____

5. diction   dictator   (decorate/edict) _____

6. manual   manufacture   (manuscript/mane) _____

7. terrarium   terrestrial   (terrible/terrace) _____

8. television   telegram   (telecast/teller) _____

9. biology   biologist   (bisect/biographer) _____

10. telescopic   telepathy   (telegraph/tale) _____

At Home: Add as many words as you can to the word families formed by Latin and Greek word parts.

Name _____

> Some words end with **-able** or **-ible**. When they are added as suffixes they change the word's meaning. Both of these suffixes mean "able to be," "capable of being," "likely to," "worthy of being," "fit for," or "tending to."

A. Think about adding *-able* or *-ible* to complete each word. Write the complete word on the line at the right.

1. cap____ _____

2. invis____ _____

3. poss____ _____

4. us____ _____

5. suit____ _____

B. Add the suffix *-able* or *-ible* to create a new word. Write the new word on the line. Then write a sentence containing that word.

6. break _____

_____

7. sense _____

_____

8. convert _____

_____

9. honor _____

_____

10. collapse _____

_____

At Home: Read a passage in a book, magazine, or newspaper. Then see how many words you can find that end in *-able* and *-ible*.

A. Read each word in column 1. Find its antonym, or the word that is most nearly opposite in meaning, in column 2. Then write the letter of that word on the line.

Column 1	Column 2
1. despair _____	**a.** hire
2. dismiss _____	**b.** clear
3. rigid _____	**c.** hope
4. elementary _____	**d.** thin or light
5. dense _____	**e.** flexible
6. murky _____	**f.** advanced

B. Complete each sentence with the correct vocabulary word from the box.

> accompany   intentions   supervise   physical   companion   bundle

7. Although he did not complete the project, his _____ were good.

8. For many people who live alone, a pet makes an excellent

_____ .

9. Grace offered to _____ Pete to the store so he would not be lonely on the long drive.

10. It is important to get some _____ exercise every day.

11. The mailman left a _____ of letters on the front step.

12. If there is no one to _____ the job, it may not be done correctly.

A. Use each of the vocabulary words in the box to make a sentence of your own.

> specimens   research   scientific   scenery   consented   ease

1. _____

2. _____

3. _____

4. _____

5. _____

6. _____

B. Write the vocabulary word that means almost the same as the underlined word or words.

> observer   scoured   inflate   guaranteed   launched   erupted

7. Hot water <u>burst forth</u> from the geyser. _____

8. After cooking breakfast, I <u>cleaned</u> the greasy pan with a sponge.

   _____

9. The scientist kept his distance from the volcano; he was acting only as a
   <u>watcher</u> from afar. _____

10. The manufacturer <u>assured</u> customers that the product would work

    properly. _____

11. The children wanted to <u>put air in</u> the balloons. _____

12. The government <u>sent off</u> a satellite into space. _____